The Smokefree Way

TAMIR TURGAL

The Smokefree Way
Read your way to stop smoking.
The most innovative, up-to-date and intelligent quit smoking method which will
lead you to become smokefree forever.

TSFW

244 5th Avenue, Suite 2320

New York, N.Y. 10001

info@smokefreeway.com

Copyright © 2013 Tamir Turgal

All rights reserved.

ISBN: 0615855121

ISBN 13: 9780615855127

Table of contents

Foreword 1

The 'Smokefree Way' Program 11

Part One: The Physical Effect

1 Between Need and Want 23

2 A Sophisticated Impersonator 31

3 A Brief Note on the Human System.................... 40

4 The Nicotine Effect.................................... 48

5 A Unique Addiction 56

6 The Transparent Enemy............................... 64

7 The Addiction Experience 70

8 Light Smokers 77

9 Physical Disturbance 82

10 Interrupting the Natural Balance 89

Part Two: The Mental Effect

1 The Psychological relation to Smoking............... 97

2 The Way Thinking Evolves in Relation to Smoking 106

3 Formation of Thinking Patterns 116

4 Stressful Situations and Chain Smoking.............. 122

5 Smoking and Concentration 130

6 Smoking and self-Confidence 133

7 Passing the Time Smoking............................ 138

8 Smoking, Enjoyment & Relaxation 142

9 Appetite Suppressant and Digestive Assistant 152

10 Aligning Thought and Action......................... 164

Part Three: Changing Course

1 The Importance of Understanding the Process....... 173

2 Changing Course 183

3 The Same Effort 197

4 Learning to Ride a Bike.............................. 202

5 Actually Stopping to Smoke......................... 207

6 Terminology.. 219

Part Four: A New and Great State

1 A Tangible improvement in the Quality of Life...... 231

2 Being Prepared For Flashbacks 238

3 A New Era.. 245

Recommendations

As someone who well knows about the problem of addiction to smoking and its consequences from first hand professional experience, I was very glad that at long last readers worldwide are being offered an innovative and unique approach that deals with smoking cessation specifically from the perspective of smokers. If you are a smoker, it is no exaggeration to say that the 'Smokefree way' might be one of the most important books you will ever read.

Dr. Yitzhak Berlovich, M.H.A. Expert in Healthcare Management

———

In the book 'The Smokefree way' you can find a fresh and original approach to setting free from cigarettes. It is said that there is none so wise as he who has experience, and indeed the author of the book is an ex-smoker who himself experienced smoking but knew to set himself totally free of it, and without the torment that is the lot of others who continue to search for the nearest ashtray.

The Smokefree way's approach to cessation is remarkably different from the approach of all the other methods that have been tried so far. There is no attempt here at moral preaching nor any usage of the deterrence and warnings by describing the diseases and other hardships that result from smoking and which we know about from other known cessation programs. Here everything flows and is entirely convincing. If I myself were a smoker, it seems to me that I would try to adopt the 'Smokefree way'.

Prof. Sela Ben Ami, Director of Sheba Medical Center's Institute of Chemical Pathology

About The Program and The Author

Tamir Turgal is a writer, jurist, public speaker and ex-smoker. While engaged in an in depth research project which led to his own personal quitting, he unearthed a unique way to set free from the distressing addiction to smoking by using exactly the same tools that created and sustained the addiction.

The 'Smokefree way' focuses on understanding the components of the addiction, creating an awareness of its physical and mental aspects which are the foundations of actually quitting. The program was developed and tried in the framework of a controlled setting over the course of about three years before it was launched commercially. This process was conducted in a way that closely resembles the usual food and drug administrations' accepted procedures.

The resulting comprehensive study is now being offered for the first time in a written format, and is the most effective guide written so far on smoking cessation. This is an outstanding program that really works. It is based on a unique approach that leads to a change in the way we experience the addiction to smoking even during the reading of the text. Along the way we reach a point of readiness to set free from smoking without any special effort, and move on calmly and positively to becoming smokefree.

Foreword

'Smokefree way' is not a cessation program that is like other programs you have probably come across in the past. Here you will not find anecdotal tips as to how to stop smoking, or a timeline describing what will happen in the days, weeks, and months after you stop. This book does not focus on the health scares that result from smoking, nor does it pry into the financial aspect of how much smoking costs the average smoker. This program is intended for those who understand that such considerations have never in any serious way helped smokers to quit, and are interested in acquiring the tools that can lead to a real change.

Though the contents of this book are indeed interesting, and in part even known to you, it is possible that in certain places you will need to really apply yourselves a bit and think things over. The 'Smokefree way' takes into account the great importance that lies in understanding the addiction to cigarettes before actually beginning to deal with cessation.

In this book we are embarking on a journey of review during most of which you will not have to think at all about the point in time when you will actually stop smoking. Understanding the factors of the addiction creates the right preparation and supplies the tools that you will be able to use at the stage when you are ready to become free.

The program's title points to the ultimate objective, getting to the stage where you can actually stop smoking – not from a position of weakness while you still have an unresolved conflict with cigarettes – but rather from a position of strength which enables you to change course and embark on a smokefree lifestyle by definition.

It is quite obvious that many of you now holding this book are somewhat suspicious of the suggestion that a book can lead you to make a change of any sort in relation to your smoking, no matter what its title may be.

The common reaction of many smokers is to make comments such as: 'what can possibly be written here that I am not already familiar with?' Or 'can anyone really know how I personally feel about smoking?'; 'Maybe I don't really want to stop smoking?'; 'Actually I enjoy smoking, well anyway at least some of the cigarettes. And with all due respect, the urge to smoke is physical, so is there really anything that I can read that could make this urge vanish? Of course not.'

There are also others who say: 'I am aware that this book comes highly recommended and is backed by stories of success through its method. I am also familiar with people who have quit smoking in the past. But mine is a different story. The fact is that so far I haven't been able to stop.'

'If we were talking about how to help me to cut down to say three or four cigarettes a day, and to smoke only the ones that I really enjoy, well that is definitely something worthwhile trying. However, to stop smoking completely, though it may well be a heart's wish, doesn't seem realistic at this point in my life. After all, there are times when I really need the cigarettes.'

'And even if there is an elegant way to quit smoking, I don't want to be left vulnerable and defenseless. Smoking for sure gives me something otherwise I wouldn't be doing it, so why should I give it up? And you know what, even if I smoke too much, and even if there is a price for that, so what? That's life. Is there anything in this world that doesn't come with a price tag?'

These are genuine arguments and there is no doubt that most of you can relate to at least some of them. Smoking cessation is one of those problems in life in which people are concerned not only about the possibility of failure but worry no less about the prospect of success. No matter how much you want to get rid of this addiction, there is a great fear out there that you will be left with a huge feeling of emptiness and that an important auxiliary tool that, at least sometimes, supports you in life's struggles, will be taken away from you.

We must take this into account. It is no wonder that breaking free from smoking is not by any means a minor task. Were it otherwise there wouldn't be so many addicts all over the world. Almost every smoker tries to quit at least once during his smoking career.

According to the research, less than five percent of the smokers who attempt to quit without some form of support succeed in doing so. This low ratio of success confirms the strong grip that this pattern has on those who smoke. Among the small percentage of ex-smokers who took the 'cold turkey' route, many had to go through it several times before stopping entirely, whilst others within this category are forced to quit by external factors. We are, undoubtedly, talking about a phenomenon that has a powerful impact on smokers.

If you are an average smoker getting through a pack a day or even, say, just fifteen, it is likely that smoking is the action you repeat most frequently on any given day. And if you work in a non-smoking environment, or refrain from smoking in your home because of your children, it is probably the main reason for your daily breaks. After years of smoking, such patterns become your lifestyle. It is not just something you do but has become part of who you are, a part of your personality.

Is there an elegant way to change this? Is there a way to become smokefree, but really free, without even thinking about cigarettes, as if we never smoked before? The answer is 'yes'. This is the way I made the transition from being a smoker to being smokefree. And this is, without a doubt, exactly the way you too are about to follow by the time you finish reading this book. But you must read the book carefully, giving it your full attention, and relate to its contents honestly.

Let's review for a moment one of the arguments we put forward earlier: the desire of many smokers to cut down their consumption to just a few cigarettes a day. What lies behind such a statement of intent? A few things. One is our acknowledgment that we smoke too much – certainly more than we would like. Another is that there are a few cigarettes that we feel give us something more than the other cigarettes we smoke.

In addition it seems to us, or at least to some of us, that cutting down the daily intake to just a few can, and should, be the best solution. It can be said that this approach is common to many smokers though it is obviously impossible to say that it applies to everyone.

One of the foundations for achieving a change in any area of our lives is a preparedness to examine our basic assumptions. When we say that we smoke too much this means that the act of smoking is not entirely what it appears to be. We are, seemingly, solely responsible for our smoking – we buy the cigarettes, go out for smoking breaks, and light the cigarettes ourselves. And yet, most of us find it simply impossible to cut down and then continue smoking at the reduced level.

As for the claim that there are some cigarettes we think give us 'more'; since all cigarettes are the same, it has to be realized that this claim in fact relates to certain situations during the day – after a meal, or while we drink a cup of coffee – rather than to something inherent in the cigarettes themselves.

The same applies to the assumption that if we could only manage to cut down to just a few cigarettes a day we could actually enjoy the best of all worlds. This perspective, which is totally understandable, reflects a feature that is unique to a smoker's point of view. Usually it refers to a more or less a pack a day smoker. It expresses an ideal concept we adopt based on the insights and beliefs that are typical of the state in which we find ourselves.

In other words, as smokers, we have formed a perception which does not enable us to even imagine a reality of complete freedom from cigarettes. From our point of view it is not practical at this point in our lives and, therefore, the ideal solution becomes 'just a few cigarettes a day.' Not because it is really the best solution, but because this is the solution that seems attainable, at least theoretically.

The truth is that for a daily smoker a complete and genuine cessation is much more realistic and attainable than cutting down the quantity. Since there is an addictive component in cigarettes, it is not possible to regulate the amount smoked. Even if we make a huge effort and manage to reduce our consumption for a while, our physical and mental systems will not be affected by that for long, and sooner or later our consumption will return to the average level it was prior to the attempt to cut down.

The 'Smokefree way', is a program that focuses mostly on understanding the addiction and the processes that lead us to form our basic assumptions. The most important issues we focus on are knowledge and awareness of what it is that keeps us smokers over the years. Our static thinking patterns in relation to our smoking are patterns we have never examined and have no clear understanding of how they were formed. These patterns are the addiction's weakest links. The 'Smokefree way' program provides us with the ultimate method of taking advantage of these weak links.

I myself started smoking at the age of seventeen. I remember that already in my early twenties I felt chained to cigarettes and knew that this was an issue I would have to deal with at some point. I had a set response which I used every time I was asked about stopping or thought about it myself: 'I will stop smoking when I'm thirty.' I used to repeat this sentence like a mantra to myself and those around me and things seemed to make sense. I am in my twenties, a young and healthy guy, why should I be bothered about my smoking? I had every reason in the world to continue enjoying the cool image, the smoking itself, and the pack of cigarette in my pocket.

I turned thirty, thirty one, then thirty two, and I kept on smoking. By then I started to understand that I was deceiving myself. I realized that during all those years I had simply been telling myself a story so that I could postpone dealing with this problem. And as long as the story made sense to me, that was enough for me to remain in denial.

Just like you I didn't even know where to begin. The idea that I would never smoke again seemed unimaginable. How disappointing it is to reach this stage in life when we really want to stop and we cease lying to ourselves, only to find that we are helpless because after years of smoking we have almost managed to forget that once we too were non-smokers. We then begin with the assumption that we are simply stuck with the cigarettes.

Another year went by. I met a friend who told me that he was trying to quit smoking and we discussed it. My initial reaction was typical. I said to him: 'Just the thought of quitting makes me so anxious that I feel compelled to light a cigarette,' and I immediately did. As much as I wanted to stop smoking, and even though I knew I had a serious problem, the very idea that I might actually succeed in quitting terrified me. My basic assumption was that life without cigarettes would mean a life of permanent emptiness and restlessness. The source of this perception is that every time we, as smokers, refrain from smoking for a while, we feel empty and increasingly stressed.

I thought that there had to be a solution. After all, I had seen people quit, though not many. Could it possibly be that so many people experience such a strong addiction without there being a realistic method of cessation available to them? That indeed seemed to be the case.

I started to explore this subject. As luck would have it, I happened then to be visiting various countries in the course of my work. I managed to utilize my spare time gathering information in libraries and other centers of information. From the extensive range of literature and works of research on the subject of the addiction, it became clear to me that despite the endless volumes of material in this field, only a small proportion relates to the perspective of the smokers themselves. Moreover, there were very few sources reflecting a real understanding of the kind of information that smokers lacked and which would enable them to deal with their smoking problem.

I wasn't interested in focusing on the data related to the dangerous effects of smoking on health. Like any other smoker, my initial preference was to avoid such material altogether. It was obvious to me that even if I studied the link between smoking and various illnesses in depth, it wouldn't make me stop smoking. I was much more interested in understanding the unique characteristics of cigarette smokers.

The more understanding I gained of the addiction itself, and the more I researched the physical and behavioral aspects of myself and of other smokers, the more I realized the extent to which this addiction relies on an almost automatic conduct of those who practice it. I reckoned that at some point in our lives most of us simply find ourselves stuck with the cigarettes without knowing how this process came into being or what it is that keeps it going day in and day out. Many smokers wake up in the morning to another day filled with smoking even though some of them say loudly and clearly that they don't want to continue smoking. Yet most do not succeed in even trying to stop. They usually say 'what's the point, it's in any case not going to work,' and they know from previous attempts that they are right.

For all of that, something happened to me that seemed at first unreal, and yet there was no denying that the basic knowledge I had acquired about what it is that activates and maintains the addiction, simply made me open my eyes. Just the relevant information, relying particularly on analyzing the reality I experience in day to day life, led me to acknowledge a simple truth – that our addiction to cigarettes is based on our ignorance. I really don't want to insult anyone, so I'd like to make it very clear that I am referring solely to our lack of information about smoking and not to any other area of our lives.

Without explaining this right now, I'll say that once we can figure out how we are affected by our cigarette smoking and by our self-definition as smokers, all the barriers and obstacles disappear. Then, within just few days we can completely change course. It's as simple as that. All we need is an understanding.

Although it is true that as the months and years go by and we continue to smoke the addiction becomes increasingly rooted, the fact is that understanding how this process works will enable us to use the very same processes that reinforce the addiction to actually be set free of it.

They say that if someone enters a minefield, the safest way for him to get out is to go back, step by step, following exactly the footprints he left behind on the way in. This is precisely the formula I used to become free of my smoking. Firstly, I made sure I correctly understood how the addiction was formed and what was responsible for maintaining it. That is to say that I carefully pinpointed my footprints, and from then on all I had to do was to take the same steps but in the opposite direction.

I don't expect you to agree with me at this stage. Nevertheless, I'll say that our intellectual capacity to review and understand the reality in which we act and into which we are maneuvered, has the potential of allowing us to see things in a broader prospective. We can then impose a preferred reality especially when it's all about our own behavioral conduct.

When dealing with our smoking there are absolutely no external elements that we are dependent on. Trust your own common sense and join me on a journey – which, by the way, is not that long – and I'll guide you on how to free yourselves form smoking and stay smokefree forever.

The 'Smokefree Way' Program

After sixteen years of smoking, I found myself becoming free of the addiction in a matter of just a few days. In the weeks and months that followed, the reality of my new found freedom, far from remaining a constant, had in fact expanded. Each day I began to wonder whether there was a way for me to assemble the information in a form that would be relevant to smokers. I wanted to stay away entirely from the health implications involved, not out of a disregard for such possible outcomes, but rather out of a clear understanding that resolving the addiction was one thing, whereas dealing with the diseases it may lead to was something else altogether. I realized that in order to help smokers to set themselves free, the focus had to be exclusively on the addiction itself and not on its potential consequences.

The question I asked myself time and again was whether it would be possible for me to present my fellow smokers, soon to be smokefree, with a coherent and structured doctrine incorporating the knowledge I had accumulated so that they too could experience the same 'miracle' I had.

I devoted a significant period of time to the preparation of the contents of the 'Smokefree way' program. I researched every aspect related to this phenomenon, starting with the initial reasons that tempt youngsters to ever start smoking and, going on from there, to the physical and mental factors that transform us – or more accurately who we once were – from occasional experimental users into lifelong smokers.

I concentrated mainly on our daily experiences, clarifying the processes involved and their impact on our insights and thinking patterns. When I had finished organizing the information, filtered out the unessential, and arranged it all in a structured form, I concluded that when presented to smokers, the process by which we are enslaved becomes very clear. All that remains then is to convey the essential instructions that will enable us to regain our freedom. The primary rule is that everything is subject to a proper understanding of the processes of the addiction.

I started to hold short cessation sessions involving two consecutive meetings, usually with a gap of a day or two between them. At these meetings I passed on the knowledge I had acquired in the format which I had prepared. The reason I decided to do this in two meetings was that it enabled me to supply the information in easy stages rather than in a massive lump. More than anything else, doing it in a phased way removed any pressure the smokers may have felt during the initial meeting.

It was obvious to me that if I were to cram it all into one long and demanding session, some of the participants might find themselves preoccupied by the thought that the 'moment of truth' was approaching, when at some point towards the end of the day they would have to take the plunge and actually stop smoking. Such tension may prevent some people from concentrating on the program itself. On the other hand, having two sessions, in the full knowledge that there was no need for anyone to stop smoking at the first meeting, had a calming effect and made it easier for everyone to relate fully to the contents of the program.

'The Smokefree way' book is based on the live session's program and differs only in that the book is a medium that enables the inclusion of even a larger amount of information.

You the readers can, of course, control the progress of your own reading and can decide on a personal level at what pace you wish to read the book. You may choose to read it all in one go, or to do it in two or more stages. Match your reading to your preferred pace as long as you don't overly extend the periods between each reading. Reading the book within a short time frame is certainly preferable.

Moreover, in the cessation meetings we conduct, we usually have smoking breaks every half an hour or so. We have these breaks also whenever someone asks for it even if no particular reason is given, or the request is made not long after the previous break. Smokers need to smoke, and as long as they are still on that side of the divide it is essential that they be enabled to smoke without any restraints being applied. This is particularly true at a time when they are busy with receiving the information and the tools that will enable them to bring the smoking era in their lives to an end.

Interestingly enough, it is common for participants in our cessation program to report that during the gap of a day or two between the first and second meetings they tend to smoke more than usual. The same phenomenon is repeated during the course of the second meeting itself. Smokers come to this session much more prepared for a change in their lives. By the time of the second meeting, and without a clear understanding of how it happened, the participants are much more highly motivated to 'go for it', something which just two days earlier had seemed impossible.

The same applies here, during your reading, the amount you smoke is totally up to you and I see no problem with you smoking the whole way through. Don't take this as a direct recommendation to smoke, but my attitude is that you should not 'jump the gun'. The end of your smoking career should evolve out of a full readiness – even a passion – to set yourself free. As long as there is no real change in your attitude towards your smoking, all your attempts to quit will tend to remain just attempts. However, if for health reasons, or any other reason, you are prohibited from smoking, then there is obviously no point in forcing yourself to do it. All in all – if you read the entire book your being set free is guaranteed.

Meetings in the 'Smokefree way' program involve a number of participants in a group since this is both doable, as well as being a more efficient way of conducting the session and creating an interesting and dynamic atmosphere. It is really nice to see how people around you are doing and to observe the way in which they too, in the end, become smokefree.

Having said that, the fact is that quitting smoking is a personal process. Everyone has his or her own understanding of, and their own private relationship to, their smoking addiction. In terms of cheering on or influencing a participant, the group, as such, has absolutely no role to play. If it did, this might have been some sort of a plus so far as the group itself was concerned, but most certainly a minus for the process itself. In order for someone to become entirely smokefree, the cessation should arise from a clear and complete recognition by each and every participant that becoming free does not depend on any external factor or reason. In that sense, reading the book is no different to being a participant in the live sessions.

In addition to the two meetings I have mentioned, we also hold a short third session intended for those who by then are smokefree. Usually, such a meeting is held between a month to three months after the first two sessions. The purpose of the follow up meeting is to maintain our achievement and enhance the insights we have already gained. It is not a mandatory meeting and many of those who participated in the program have absolute confidence in their ability to remain smokefree without any additional support. However, this third meeting is highly recommended, particularly for the younger participants who are more exposed to peer pressure. While readers of the book will have no need for such a repetition, nevertheless reading the book again after a period of freedom could be essential.

Perhaps the program's name 'Smokefree way' may not strike you as being particularly unique or unexpected. Yet in my view it delivers a very powerful and new message. Once, when I was on a flight, I noticed the flight attendant soon after takeoff reciting the standard instructions to the passengers which included, as has become the norm these days with airlines, the announcement that 'this is a smokefree flight.' It instantly occurred to me that this sounded a bit like 'a smokefree life' and this is exactly what our program is all about.

It is important that you realize, my fellow smokers, that your smoking is not the only issue we need to overcome. In practice, ceasing to smoke is the outcome of our freedom from the addiction and, therefore, cessation is relevant only towards the end of the program. It is of course 'the icing on the cake' and the real benefit of our newly found freedom. However, we are not simply looking for a mechanical way to enable us to stop smoking but also, and most importantly, we are involved in gaining an understanding of the factors that compel us to keep on smoking. As we shall see these factors are, by their very nature, completely different from what they appear to be on the surface.

Our preoccupation with smoking stems from physical urges and is very much determined by our thinking patterns.

By neutralizing these sources of attraction, our activities and habits related to our smoking will be necessarily eliminated. Neutralizing these factors means a transition to a life that is simply smokefree. In becoming smokefree we are, in effect, removing the smoking component from our lives. This is similar to other things we are used to saying without paying special attention to them, as when we say 'sugar-free' to mean a food that contains no sugar, or 'duty-free' when talking of a product that is not taxed.

Smokefree means living the way we once did before we became addicted, when we were completely free of that thing. This freedom is what is of vital importance, whereas the actual cessation of smoking is merely a mechanical achievement and need not preoccupy us in any way at this stage. As you will discover later on when the time comes, quitting smoking will, surprisingly, be an experience that you will actually look forward to putting into practice. Sounds unbelievable? What about living a totally smokefree life? Can you even imagine such a thing? Of course not. Well, you don't have to imagine this either. All you'll have to do is to read and think things over.

The program has succeeded beyond my expectations. Apart from the 'thank you' letters and the enthusiastic comments that I have received, I've seen how many of those who have participated in the program come to the follow up sessions just so as to show their appreciation and thank me in person for nothing less than saving their lives. My consistent response is that despite the program's very impressive success rate, and with so many participants who are today entirely smokefree, I believe that I personally never weaned even one single smoker from his addiction.

Becoming free of the addiction is exclusively the result of an action undertaken by the smokers themselves. I may have the honor of being considered as the one who opened the door and pointed toward the way out, but my role has been no more than that. I have never pushed anyone to take this path, and I certainly don't believe there is anyone who can wean another from their addiction.

Whenever I hear of various kinds of therapists with "special energies" and other such pretentious claims, I always say that aside from the fact that what they propose has no real foundation, those who succeeded in stopping to smoke after such treatments have done so despite the therapist and not because of them. There may be instances, though they are quite rare, in which some smokers have attained a unique mental state that makes them ripe for cessation and yet remain unaware of the fact that quitting is an act that is entirely up to them.

For such smokers, the mere belief that the therapist has supposedly done something to them is enough to get them going. They do not realize that, in fact, the therapist has done nothing and that advising someone after a so called treatment to 'drink lots of water, clean up your ashtrays, and never smoke again' requires no great wisdom. A smoker who tries to obey such instructions and fails to do so, is inevitably made to feel guilty for having not followed the therapist's instructions. In almost every session of the 'Smokefree way' there are those who have fallen victim to such methods.

Such treatments will not lead the vast majority of smokers to quit. Even those who do eventually stop by such means are in no way immune to the possibility that they will go back to smoking. This is because it appears that someone else was responsible for their 'success' – a success in which they seemingly played no active role.

The 'Smokefree way' program operates differently. In the same way you became smokers in the first place – only by yourselves – so too the ability and responsibility of setting yourselves free is entirely in your hands. It is dependent solely on your acquiring the relevant knowledge. The cessation is, in fact, a transition toward a new reality, and your smoking history will turn out to have been an era in your life that you are leaving behind out of a new found awareness and as a matter of personal choice. There exists no better immunity than that to guarantee that you will remain smokefree permanently.

The 'Smokefree way' involves neither reverse brain-washing nor any constant repetition of the same ideas. The program deals with the various different issues related to the smoking addiction and progresses as a single journey that passes through a number of stations along the way. On the very few occasions when a certain idea repeats itself, or when a point we have already dealt with is mentioned again, it is done within a specific context that requires such a repetition.

To achieve the desired result we aim to present a comprehensive view of the subject via the unique perspective of a smoker, and to relate only to issues that help us to become free. You will probably have noticed that in my writing I frequently address you in the first person, so that what I write comes through to you as the words and thoughts of a smoker, someone who genuinely empathizes with what another smoker is experiencing.

I am indeed an ex-smoker and yet, in delivering the program I intentionally allow myself in my mind to revert back to the time when I was a smoker and discuss the issues from the perspective of a smoker. After all, as smokers we all experience the same sensations and feelings and we all face the same difficulties. The differences between smokers lie mainly in the extent of the impact that smoking has on them.

As many ex-smokers who have participated in the program often tell me, this is perhaps one of the most appealing aspects of the 'Smokefree way'. As some of them put it to me: 'I felt that a smoker, like myself, was talking to me, and not another of those do-gooders who are constantly trying to tell you how you should live your life.' It seems that whenever the knowledge is conveyed by someone who is basically within our peer group, it helps us to openly examine the issues without barriers.

The 'Smokefree way' is an intellectually contemplative program that views the act of cessation as a unified whole. We don't put forward worthless suggestions or supply superficial tips for quitting. Our goal is to change the way in which we perceive our smoking based on a systematic and focused grasp of the issues.

Once you have fully understood the addiction, you will discover that your interaction with smoking, and the extent of your dependence on cigarettes, changes at a point at which we have barely yet touched on the issue of cessation itself. At a later stage we go on to deal with our transition to becoming smokefree and the actions and techniques we need to adopt in order to begin that process. However, we only reach that stage after we have collected sufficient knowledge and created a firm awareness.

It's a magnificent method that works in a sophisticated way that avoids a direct confrontation with smoking as such. Instead, we focus on understanding the basis of what lies beneath the surface of our smoking so that we don't have to feel pressured or inconvenienced as we progress along the way. It is as if we are flying under the addiction's radar. Once we finally reach the stage of acknowledging the physical and mental aspects of our addiction, we are then ready to set ourselves free from smoking without having to make a great effort and without any fear holding us back.

The contents of this program are quite interesting and relate to the processes that smokers go through on a daily basis. You may be familiar with some of the information while some of it will definitely be new to you. However, addressing these matters in a concentrated way and in the right order does the work and enables us to get to the right level of readiness in a secure and peaceful way. It is never too late to earn your freedom back, and it doesn't matter how many years you have already been smoking.

Professor Y. Leibowitz once said that 'it is impossible for anyone to not know and understand what they already know and understand.' In the context of our subject, it means that by revealing the relevant information and carefully familiarizing ourselves with the problem we are dealing with, we are creating a new balance of power. This enhances our ability to solve the problem in a way we couldn't do previously.

In any situation where we want to succeed and the way to that success eludes us, the acquisition of knowledge is a crucial step toward achieving it. Hence the saying 'Knowledge is power'. The 'Smokefree way' program empowers us to exploit the most valuable skill we have – the ability to learn and use the knowledge and understanding gained in order to shape for ourselves the lifestyle we want to.

Part One:

The Physical Effect

CHAPTER 1

Between Need and Want

Do we smoke out of a need or a want? The question of what motivates us to act in a certain way is one of the most interesting aspects of human conduct. There are two possible motives for our behavioral actions. One is need and the other is want. Nothing we do falls outside of these two categories. We either do something because we need to do it or because we want to do it. For many this differentiation is not clear and understanding the difference is an important starting point in our passage toward understanding our addiction to cigarettes.

First of all it has to be said that a 'need' in this context signifies something that is basically a physical necessity. We need to breathe, to eat and drink, to sleep, and to remove waste from our bodies. Without fulfilling our basic needs we simply cannot exist. The true meaning of 'need' is that whether we like it or not it is something we *must* do. We can abstain from eating for a couple of days and sometimes for even longer. We can permit ourselves to go without sleep for a period of time or dive into a pool and stop breathing while under water. It's possible. But to completely stop breathing or to permanently go without food, drink, or sleep is clearly impossible. We can say that when a particular need arises we have no choice – we must attend to it. Though we can, to an extent, manipulate our needs, we absolutely cannot ignore them altogether or decide that from now on we will operate our lives differently.

Our daily needs somewhat constrain us because they force us to free up time so that we can attend to them. If, for example, it was possible for us to give up our need for sleep, the amount of time available to us during our lives would increase by about a third. Similarly, were it possible for us to go without food we would save a great deal of time and energy as a result of our no longer having to apply resources and effort to securing the food we consume. Nevertheless, our needs serve a purpose and are good for us. They play an essential role in the process of life by ensuring that the proper functioning and balance of the body is safeguarded. The fulfillment of these needs results in our continually maintaining our bodies in good condition and in balance.

As distinct from our needs there are our wants. However, the motives that drive us to indulge in an act of want are the opposite of what compels us to fulfill a need. A want is not an inevitability; it does not result from an inner impulse and is dependent only on itself. An individual may want to have a certain career, to have a particular spouse that he likes, to travel to wherever he wants, to choose where he wants to live, or have a certain lifestyle, and so on. We can change our minds in relation to our choices or cease to want those things we originally wanted. Unlike needs, wants are not obligatory. We can say that a want expresses a choice we are making whereas a need expresses an obligation that we must fulfill.

Sometimes we don't properly differentiate between want and need. We have grown used to mixing up these two concepts because in general we don't find ourselves in a contradiction between them. As we come to the end of a day and our bodies signal feelings of tiredness, the clear implication is that we need and are obliged to sleep. At the same time, given that we conduct our lives in line with this limitation, it is also reasonable to assume that to sleep in such circumstances is also something that we would want to do. Often, when talking about all of our actions, we tend to say that we want to do them – want to sleep, want to eat, want to drink, and so on.

THE THREE CHARACTERISTICS

Distinguishing between need and want requires us to identify three characteristics in any given need. If one or more of these characteristics is missing the act would have to be considered a want and not a need.

The first characteristic of a need is the feeling that we have to do it. As the need arises within, it is clear to us that this is something we must do. The second characteristic is the sense of pressure that we feel as a result of restraining ourselves from doing it. If we refrain from fulfilling a need then, as time passes, we will experience mounting pressure and difficulty in functioning normally. The third characteristic of a need is the relief we experience when it is fulfilled. The more persistent we are in our fixed and regular fulfillment of the need, the more we will gain a feeling of balance and relief.

Let's illustrate this using sleep as an example. We know that sleep is one of the obligations we have to fulfill because it is impossible to live without sleeping. Sleep also embodies the second characteristic; if we refrain from sleeping for too long we'll become increasingly tired and feel a mounting sense of distress. As for the third characteristic, that too is to be found in the act of sleep. When we make sure that in our daily lives we sleep for a sufficient number of hours on a regular basis, we feel in balance and are able to function properly.

When we talk about a want, the situation is different. It can be shown that every 'want' lacks at least one of these three characteristics. If, for example, someone wants to play chess, they don't really have to play. In so far as a person's physical wellbeing is concerned, playing chess is not an existential requirement even if he loves the game deeply. If he doesn't play for several months, or even years, his general state will not deteriorate. He will undoubtedly miss the game and he may perhaps become a little sad, but he can nonetheless continue to lead his life in a normal way.

This introduction enables us to check whether, so far as smokers are concerned, smoking is a need or a want. The question is of course addressed to those who are active smokers as opposed to those who are at the stage of trying out smoking and are just having their first few puffs.

We were all once non-smokers. As such, we had no need, and in most cases no desire, to smoke. At some point in our lives we wanted to 'try it' and see what it was all about. This was in the form of an experiment which was clearly a want rather than a need. Cigarettes were not then a part of our lives. In the main we wanted to find out what the experience of smoking was all about – we had no long term plan.

The question here is whether, after many months or years of smoking, we relate to our daily act as a need, or whether it remains a want as it was in the beginning. Given that in our day to day speech these two concepts are frequently mixed up, we are used to getting a range of answers to this question from the participants at our meetings. Some say it is 'a need'. Others say it is 'a want'. There are those who say that it is both a want and a need and there are additional variations.

The answer is that smoking is experienced by us as a need. Although it is unique in that it is not a natural need of ours but rather one that we ourselves created, smoking is, nonetheless, both in practice and in the way we experience it, a need.

Let's try and test this according to the three characteristics that have already been mentioned. The first is the feeling of obligation. Although smoking is not a necessity in the same way as are our natural needs, every smoker feels in the course of his personal experience that he must smoke. The true meaning of 'obligation' is that there is no possibility of choice. Had the personal experience been different and without the feeling of obligation, it would have been possible for every smoker to decide to stop whenever he wanted to. As smokers we often say 'I must have a cigarette' – our subjective feeling being that we need it.

The second characteristic of a need is that if left unfulfilled we experience growing pressure and distress. And indeed anyone who is compelled to abstain from smoking for a time, for example during a flight or for any other reason, or tries to stop without proper guidance, knows how, with the passage of time, it becomes more and more difficult to go without. We have all at some time or another observed the interesting phenomenon of groups of smokers finally being able to light up immediately upon leaving the airport terminal no matter how cold and rainy or hot and humid it is outside. As time passes, the difficulty of abstaining becomes an increasing burden and it continues to be so until the smoker gets the first opportunity to smoke once again and calm his system.

The third characteristic of this need is that the more we fulfill it in a consistent and regular way, meaning that as long as we are smoking on a regular basis, it gives us a feeling of balance without our being particularly stressed.

THE FUNDAMENTAL DIFFERENCE

In our experience, smoking is indeed perceived by us as a need. But in contrast to our natural needs this need is different and the difference between them is fundamental. Our natural needs are essential to our ability to function properly; they are beneficial to us. Smoking, on the other hand, lessens our ability to function properly and is harmful to us.

Our natural needs are part and parcel of the way in which we were created and as such we have no control or choice in the matter. This is the way in which the human body systems and needs are structured and it is good that it is so. On the other hand, the need to smoke is one that we ourselves have created. From that we can deduce that putting an end to that need is also in our hands.

The need to smoke is not a genuine need, though it is true that so far as smokers are concerned smoking is in fact perceived as a need. However, it is a need that we created inadvertently and unintentionally. Therefore, when we come to understand this need and the way in which it was formed, we will soon see that through a not particularly complicated process it is possible to eliminate it and be set free from it.

As mentioned, our needs restrict us – a fact that is expressed by our obligation that compels us to invest time and resources in fulfillment of those needs. At the same time, it is clear to us that our natural needs are a requirement that enables us to function properly and that they are of benefit to us.

We have to realize the fact that on the one hand every need that is not genuine restricts us, but that we don't really require it in order to live a better life. In fact, generally speaking, this self-created need will only be a burden in our lives. It will take up our time and resources and harm our natural state of balance.

The significance of a natural need is that we have no choice in the matter. It's an obligation. But when the need is not genuine this obligation is nothing more than a form of enslavement. It means that in order to continue to function properly we are dependent on an additional factor and that we are less our own masters.

Our natural needs represent a necessary minimum and are intended to put us in balance and to preserve our ability to continue to function normally in our lives. Adding yet another restraining need, such as smoking, that damages our natural balance and demands resources such as money to buy cigarettes and time, cannot be a rational objective for anyone to try and achieve. And indeed every smoker finds himself one day simply stuck with this need. No one who is just starting to smoke takes into account the heavy price he will be paying and the state of enslavement he is entering into.

But in all of this there is also good news. Need and want are not in conflict with one another. Despite the very common mistake, the idea of 'willpower' is not relevant to being set free from smoking. Ceasing to smoke is not dependent on this particular power. When we need to fulfill a certain need, trying to use our willpower against it is utterly pointless.

Examples of this are the failed attempts of smokers to reduce the number of cigarettes they smoke. The physical need to smoke continues, and to negate that need, smokers apply significant willpower to restrain themselves from smoking for periods longer than they are used to. During all of these intervals between one cigarette and another, the urge to smoke doesn't decrease. On the contrary, it increases and is accompanied by feelings of stress and frustration. This process resembles a bout of arm wrestling in which neither side lets go. Even if the smoker succeeds in continuing the struggle for a time, at the end of it there is an inevitable return to smoking the usual number of cigarettes.

In order for us to put an end to this self-created need, we have to go about it in an altogether different way. That way is founded on a process which terminates the need by using the same implements which created it in the first place. It is a way that can be acquired calmly and with ease in the course of the journey on which we are embarking together with this book.

CHAPTER 2

A Sophisticated Impersonator

The nicotine that is in the tobacco leaves we smoke is basically a poisonous substance widely used in agriculture as an insecticide. In nature, nicotine is mainly to be found in the tobacco plant and it is probable that, as part of the plant's survival mechanism, nicotine helps to protect it against harmful insects. There are also various other plants that function on the same principle.

Nicotine and other active substances of this sort that are to be found in such plants are generally termed 'psychoactive', due to their capacity to influence the functioning of the brain. An animal that tries to eat a plant that contains a psychoactive substance is likely to harm its nervous system. Even in instances where such harm is only temporary, the unpleasant experience apparently makes an impression which will deter the animal from trying to eat such a plant in the future.

We, on the other hand, by consuming nicotine through the smoking of cigarettes, are receiving this substance in a milder form after the tobacco leaves have already been processed and dried. From the moment we light a cigarette and inhale the smoke into our lungs, a small quantity of nicotine enters the blood stream and from there reaches our brain.

The uniqueness of this substance is expressed in its ability to at all reach the brain and in the way in which it succeeds in disrupting our chemical balance. This effect begins a few seconds after the first inhalation of the cigarette we have lit, and many smokers are well aware of the almost immediate sense of relief they experience at that moment. It is something we feel in a more obvious way in situations in which we have been prevented from smoking for a while and at long last go for a cigarette break after having already felt under pressure to have a smoke. As said, this sense of relief begins to be felt literally a few seconds after the first intake of smoke.

Nicotine is a psychoactive drug and it is this drug that is responsible for smokers' dependence on cigarettes. If you look closely at the range of different types of cigarettes on display on shop shelves, you will see that the common denominator between them all is that they are all made from tobacco leaves. Apart from a very few alternatives that are not at all popular, there isn't a brand of cigarettes containing the dried leaves of some other plant. This is not accidental; substances to be found in tobacco leaves – together with the nicotine – are what cause the effects we have mentioned.

The addiction to cigarettes is generally regarded as one of the strongest of addictions. The meaning of the term 'strong addiction' is that the dependence the user develops to the nicotine in cigarettes is very powerful. It is relevant to ask why, in this particular instance, where the drug is quite weak so that it is almost unnoticeable, such a strong dependence nevertheless develops?

The ongoing daily consumption conditions us to function under varying degrees of tension. Every time our level of nicotine drops the tension gradually rises, becoming a kind of reminder that triggers us to have another cigarette. This process works in a way that really resembles the natural functioning of the body's system. Meaning that when there is a shortage or a need of some kind it is followed by a reminder to fill that shortage.

If we are talking about a lack of sleep – we would feel a sense of tiredness overcoming us. If we are in need of food or drink – hunger and thirst would be the reminders. If the need arises to remove a surplus of liquids from our body – we would feel a pressure to do so. Nicotine 'wraps' itself around exactly the same mechanism – every time there is a drop in the level of nicotine in the blood, a slight feeling of distress begins to be felt which is a sort of reminder to us of that decrease.

Similarly to the way in which our natural needs manifest themselves, the feelings of shortage and craving are at first very slight. Only with the passage of time as the shortage is not filled, does the feeling of unease increase. So it is with hunger and thirst, and so it is also with our craving to smoke.

This is also the way in which filling the shortage is managed. In a way that is similar to the management of our natural needs, so too with nicotine; we don't wait too long nor do we unnecessarily prolong the wait before filling the shortage. With food it is expressed in the eating of our regular meals: normally, we try to ensure that we don't starve ourselves before finally eating. With our need for sleep it is expressed by creating a routine for the number of hours we regularly sleep: in this area too we don't needlessly 'overstretch' ourselves. So it is also with smoking: A slight tingle caused by a lack of nicotine will most of the time be quickly responded to.

This is expressed by the pack of cigarettes which we smoke daily, or less than a pack for those who smoke less, or more than one pack for those who smoke more. Each of us decides for themselves how many meals a day they eat and the amount of food that is sufficient for them, and everyone one of us develops a routine of sleeping a more or less regular number of hours per day. In the same way, every smoker becomes used to regularly smoking a certain number of cigarettes every day.

If, for example, we get used to drinking a lot every day, we would have to see to it that we remove the surplus quantities of liquid from our bodies at more regular intervals. Our body will become used to the situation and the processes of discharge will operate more intensely so that we will feel more pressed to relieve ourselves more often every day. Similarly, when we start to consume cigarettes, our system begins to become used to the situation, and there starts to develop within us an over sensitivity in relation to the lack of nicotine between one cigarette and another.

The feelings of craving are very easily aroused and create an immediate trigger to smoke in order to ease the sense of tension. As time passes over the years, we become less and less willing to endure these feelings of craving and irritability resulting from the lack of nicotine in our system. In accordance with this reality we accustom ourselves to hurry up and rectify this lack. Above all else, this phenomenon confirms that we have become weaker. Without being sufficiently tolerant, we hurry to ease these unpleasant feelings brought about by the shortage of nicotine.

THE BASIS FOR FULFILLING A NATURAL NEED

If we look at this a little bit more closely we will discover big differences between the various reasons that lead us to fulfill a need. When talking about an essential need that has to be fulfilled such as food or sleep, for example, the main reason for filling the shortage is to get energy – something we are used to calling 're-charging our batteries.' We are required to renew our strengths through eating and sleeping.

Though there is also the factor of preventing feelings of unease, it is not the dominant factor. We eat regularly first of all in order to gain energy and strength and not because of a great fear of feeling hunger. Usually, we try to avoid reaching the point of feeling very hungry. And if, nonetheless, we reach a stage when we do feel a strong urge to eat, it is possible to define it as an activation of our body organs' 'alarm systems' signaling their urgent need for new energy.

Our body is built to work in such a way that when there is an essential need to be filled there will be feelings of unease within the organs of our body, the purpose of which is to alert us and prevent any possibility of our ignoring this distress. This is important in that it doesn't enable us to forget our need to fill the shortage and the risk of us becoming utterly exhausted. The 'hunger feel' enables us to avoid such a possibility so that as time passes the feeling becomes increasingly bothersome and therefore impossible to ignore.

That having been said, since we are talking about a natural and essential process that develops gradually, we don't become frightened or pressured immediately the feelings of hunger or tiredness begin to be felt. We are aware that we have room in which to maneuver and a reasonable amount of time until the feelings of shortage really begin to distress us.

When we talk about our natural needs, the fact is that they are not aroused without a reason. If there is a feeling of hunger it is a sign that there is a real need to restore the body's energy. If there is a feeling of tiredness, it is a sign that one really has to enable the body to rest. As we all know, the natural human structure is well planned.

There are two important aspects to a genuine need. One is that the feeling involved is merely a reminder and not the main issue. The main aspect of eating is that we received what was missing and not the fact that we have eased the hunger itself. The second aspect is that for every one of us, even when there is a delay in the fulfillment of an essential need, it is preferable that we do not become stressed by such a delay and that we do not become excessively irritable because of it. If we have to attend to the provision of food, rest, and clean air to breathe, it is desirable that we nonetheless be in a reasonable state so that we can act in an appropriate way in attaining these objectives. Excessive restlessness or panic will not help us to restore what is missing. Therefore when there is a reasonable delay in the fulfillment of our natural needs, we are built to cope with the reality without becoming too pressured.

THE BASIS FOR FULFILLING A NON-GENUINE NEED

With cigarettes, on the other hand, the need for nicotine is not a genuine need. Filling the shortage that has been created offers no physical benefit other than perhaps a temporary relief from the craving itself. Indeed, it is precisely in the fulfillment of such a non-genuine need that we should be much more in control of our actions. After all, we are not short of anything. Thus, if we didn't fulfill this apparent need nothing would in fact happen to us.

But surprisingly, in the case of smoking, the unease and irritability that we feel as a result of the craving for a cigarette, are felt as a kind of suffering which it is really hard for us to endure. Hence it is this virtual shortage that becomes very threatening. On the face of it, this situation appears to be very strange, but in fact it is pretty logical.

When the need is not genuine and the feeling of a lack is not a reminder of something else but is itself the major issue, it serves as a reminder to itself. This feeling of shortage is responsible both for the creation of the problem and also for its solution – having another cigarette – leading to a temporary respite that puts the feeling of shortage in suspense for a little while longer. In such a situation there is no real sense of serenity. Every lull in our feelings of shortage and unease are merely a prelude to the return of the same feelings which will begin to be felt within half an hour of the cigarette being smoked. What we have here is an incessant series of recurrences and we get used to relying on the periods of respite between cigarettes.

This is the significance of the weakening mentioned earlier. Instead of the sense of strength and security that is implanted within us by nature, we become dependent on the feeling of relief that will follow the next cigarette. The alarm system has been activated over nothing.

Moreover, in comparison to our natural needs, this process is accelerated both in terms of the speed at which we begin to feel increasingly distressed between one cigarette and another, as well as in terms of the frequency with which this feeling is repeated in the course of a day. No natural need of ours is aroused so many times a day and so quickly between one time and the next. It is, therefore, little wonder that we have no room for maneuver when it comes to the non-genuine need for nicotine. Over the years we have grown used to the fact that the single way to ease the distress caused by cigarettes is to have another dose of nicotine. When we are unable to do that, or when we are late in supplying the body with this additional dose, we very rapidly become stressed.

LAST CIGARETTES IN THE PACK

There is an even more extreme phenomenon, when not all of the cigarettes in the pack have yet been smoked but the pack is just about to be empty. Already then smokers begin to feel the pressure. Already then we begin to think and be bothered by the thought of where the next pack is going to come from. That is the extent to which the apprehension of being short of nicotine frightens us.

It's interesting, we haven't yet finished the cigarettes that are still in the pack, we still have one or two cigarettes left, and sometimes even a bit more than that, and we are nevertheless already agitated. Why is that? Are we afraid that if we don't manage to smoke in time something will happen to us? Definitely not! The fear is not of some danger but rather of the unpleasant experience of the feelings of craving and distress.

We mentioned earlier that this is one of the strongest known addictions. It stems from the persistent daily supply of nicotine to the body. Such persistence is what also at one and the same time creates both the craving and the pretense of relieving it. This reality weakens us and activates our body systems in an improper way. And this continuous process that goes on for years and years leads to a constant weakening, both physical and psychological.

There is an unwritten code among smokers that you don't take the last cigarette from someone else's pack. That is to say, if you are left without any and you ask someone to give you a cigarette and notice that that person has only one smoke left, taking it violates the code. The acceptable norm is that the last cigarette in the pack has to remain there to be smoked by its owner. The logic is that it is this cigarette which enables him now to have a last dose of nicotine.

Yes, smokers well understand the significance of 'being stuck without cigarettes'. This code of behavior evolved in order to ensure that a smoker who has only one cigarette left, will be absolved from helping another smoker in distress. In certain situations, when sources of supply are not so readily available, as in a remote village or during a hike in open countryside, even if the smoker has a few cigarettes left they will acquire the same status as a 'last cigarette' has. This is another good example illustrating the extent to which the dependency on cigarettes becomes stronger as the smoker becomes weaker.

CHAPTER 3

A Brief Note on the Human System

We live in a world which, from the point of view of the phenomena occurring within it, is a truly wondrous place. Because we were born into this already established reality, many of us have grown to accept it as it is and tend not to devote too much thought to it. However, in order to acquire the relevant knowledge that will free us from smoking, we need to look briefly at this reality, its link to our sustainability as humans, and understand how it works. It is there that the unique process that keeps us as smokers is hidden. When we uncover this process the solution to our smoking problem will also be clearly understood.

Suppose that the American space agency NASA had been capable of developing the perfect space exploration vehicle. Suppose that such a vehicle could have been landed on a distant star and functioned there as it was designed to do – searching for data, acquiring knowledge, and surviving in differing climatic conditions. Had such a vehicle been developed it would, to a large extent, have greatly resembled the human body. For this is precisely how our human body operates. We received as a gift a vehicle that travels across a star known as 'Earth'.

Our body has arms and legs which provide efficient leverage enabling us to move from place to place and allow us to hold on to things, maintain balance as needed, climb hills and rock faces, swim, crawl, jump and run, ascend and descend. We can do almost anything we want to do. Our space vehicle is equipped with extraordinarily sophisticated systems which are capable of collecting information and adjusting the body to differing external conditions. It also possess a highly developed optical system which enables the human eye to accurately adjust its sight between objects near and far, and do so at great speed. In addition, we are endowed with an intricate and efficient hearing system, a sense of smell, a sense of taste, and a sense of touch that, in effect, extends across our entire body and is a super sensory device enabling us to adapt ourselves to differing external environmental conditions.

This information reveals nothing new, I am aware of that. And yet it is such a pity that we generally don't pause to examine the world around us more closely. When we observe life in this world we see that everything has a reason and a purpose. All the unique traits possessed by the various species of creatures that inhabit our planet are intended to achieve an objective. There is nothing that lacks reason and logic to justify its existence.

First and foremost the overriding goal is, of course, survival. All our body systems are at our disposal to enable us to deal properly with an ever changing environmental reality. Going back to the analogy of the space vehicle, in order for it to be regarded as ideal, the first condition must surely be that it is capable of surviving for a long period of time on the star on which it is destined to be and function – in our case, planet earth. This is the general objective without which it is entirely impossible to function.

But there are other more specific objectives that relate to the quality of our performance on planet earth. Meaning that it is not enough for the space vehicle to simply survive. It also has to function efficiently on its star. Our body's systems have to perform correctly in order for us to achieve our objectives in the most efficient way. If, for example, we want to travel the world and discover new places, we must be in good physical shape so that we can walk well. We must also not be hungry, meaning that we should have enough energy – fuel – in our bodies to enable us to function properly and not be too weak to carry out the tasks we have set for ourselves.

A perfect system, besides having to include mechanisms and sensors that will ensure its survivability, must also be simple to operate, easy to maintain, not require too much energy, have internal systems for self repairs in the event of a breakdown, and other such features. These are all attributes that we humans were handed as a gift.

Earlier on we talked about the importance of the knowledge and awareness that will enable us to become smokefree. Though in this chapter we are relating to a more general perspective of the reality, this outlook is a basis and a preparation for an understanding of the factors that shape and influence our attitude toward smoking. Observing the way in which we experience the physical reality helps us to gauge our personal place within that reality, and is a vital stage in the quest to achieve our ultimate objective.

Our body system is simple to operate. In fact, it is so simple that in everything related to our internal organs and their interdependence we are completely exempted from having to consciously activate or look after them. For example, there is no need for us to be involved with the functioning of the various organs of our digestive system that manage the food we eat – our fuel. It is as if the body knows when to digest and how to deliver the various components to where they need to be.

Besides that we also get oxygen through our lungs from the air we breathe. The oxygen is taken in a unique way via the red cells in our blood and is channeled to all our organs. Every organ is in need of oxygen for its existence. The blood carrying the oxygen, and all the other required substances, circulates through a complicated network of pipelines which are our arteries, veins, and very small blood vessels. The flow of blood through these 'pipes' is induced by the operation of the heart – a powerful pump that continues to function throughout our lives.

All this happens automatically. We have no conscious control over these matters and we don't need to intentionally decide or act in order for all the components to operate in a perfectly coordinated way.

To invent a space vehicle such as this, a vehicle that is turned on only once during its lifetime and is programmed to operate complex procedures in a fully coordinated way, is quite a sophisticated operation. But that is only the tip of the iceberg. In order that the human species can function and develop, it has to be equipped with a broad range of even more advanced and efficient systems.

It is important, for example, that the structure be easy to maintain. And that indeed is so. Today, we are living in an era commonly termed as the age of plenty. But for thousands of years people lived in an environment in which there was far less access to sources of food, water and clothing. There were no supermarkets or department stores in which clothes could be bought, nor any residential buildings supplied with electricity, water and heating. Nonetheless, people managed, and sometimes managed rather well.

Today, in the modern world, we suffer from the fact that our bodies are weighed down by over eating or a lack of exercise. But as a general rule our body makes no great demands on us; it requires not to be over fed, supplied with enough water to drink, given some exercise and allowed to breathe clean air – preferably from a non-urban area. That is all. Most of the problems and illnesses suffered by man stem from improper maintenance rather than from some defect in our very impressive body system.

We are now about to deal a little bit more deeply with our body system and especially with the functioning of one particular organ which is the command and control center of our entire body – an organ that I metaphorically refer to as the cockpit – our brain. There is no intention here of giving a lesson in anatomy, definitely not. But as we progress you will see that everything connects up and the picture becomes clearer. The very fact that we are dealing with a topic that involves getting to know the world can, in and of itself, be a source of optimism since it leads us to recognize how magnificent the world we live in really is.

THE UNIQUENESS OF THE BRAIN

The nervous system extends to almost every area of our bodies. Many people are unaware that the brain is actually part of this system and is its central organ. There is a physical connection between the brain and the spinal cord and from there a connection to the entire nervous system – which is to say to the whole body. Apart from the way in which this unique organ controls our physical bodies, the brain's function is of course also linked to the part that is responsible for our processes of thought. Even though our thoughts are an abstract notion and cannot be traced to any part of our body, we are certainly able to identify a connection between our thoughts and the functioning of the brain. Nowadays, with advanced scanning devices, we can identify activity in various areas of the brain linked to processes of thought, memory, imagination and the like.

The point I wish to emphasize at this stage relates to the characteristics of the link that exists between the brain and the body at a quite basic level. As a general rule, the management of the body's affairs are handled by the brain and the nervous system. The brain is the command and control center of our body. As is typical with any command center it requires, at the very least, two vitally important processes: A flow of information into the command center itself, and a way of processing that data and thereby generating a response.

The data as to the external environmental conditions reaches the brain through multiple sensory spots scattered on the skin of the body as well as through sight, hearing, taste and sense of smell. There are also sensors that are responsible for balance which supply data as to the stability of our bodies and there are still other activities apart from those we have so far mentioned. In addition, there are also internal sensors that provide information about various processes within our bodies. In this way information is transmitted to the brain regarding a shortage of liquids or foods as well as breathing, heartbeat and other actions that our nervous system keeps a check on.

In part, this function is accomplished unconsciously, meaning that the brain and the nervous system also manage the body's affairs regardless of our awareness. For example, our body systems continue to function also when we are asleep. To an extent, however, there is an interconnection between the information that reaches the brain and our awareness.

What a space vehicle! Everything is carefully planned down to the last detail so that a person is always pointed in the direction of balance. If something is lacking, the systems are programmed to signal a warning so that the lack can be rectified. The whole structure of needs we talked about earlier aims to safeguard a proper and balanced maintenance. Balance for an individual is the optimal state and the one in which we can think most clearly, function most efficiently, and gain more enjoyment out of life.

It is customary to say that people appreciate things only when they feel they are missing. Yet it is true that we tend not to appreciate enough and be enthusiastic enough about that sophisticated body of ours, which is continuously at our service. At times we even neglect or damage it, though even in this we are beneficiaries – the body's systems are not easily harmed.

The processes that take place in the brain produce hormones and chemical fluids. This is not the place to explain these processes in depth. However, we will take a look at just a few points related to the link between these processes and the context of our actions.

In the brain, as the command and control center, use is made of the chemical substances that influence the various sensations we have in our bodies. Let's, as an example, deal with the senses of hunger and satiation. As we have seen, physical sensations are signs that help us to fulfill our bodily needs. There are sensors in the brain that, together with additional organs of the body, activate the sense of hunger. This feeling that we sometimes recognize by a sense of emptiness and a growling stomach, alerts us to act in a conscious way to return to the body the energy it requires – in other words to feed it.

The feeling of satiation we get after eating is also part of this mechanism. In the same way that there are processes responsible for the sense of hunger so there is, at the other end of the spectrum, a system that is in charge of the feeling of satiation when the body has obtained the food it was demanding. This balance is, of course, important since it enables us to know when it is time to stop eating.

CHAPTER 4

The Nicotine Effect

So far we have been talking in general terms about the way in which our body systems function, and the importance of the brain in managing the body's affairs. We said that our body systems do not damage easily. Sadly, however, they are not completely immune. There are substances that can penetrate our body's natural defenses and influence the way we function. Nicotine is one such substance.

When the nicotine reaches the brain it alters its chemical balance. It is important to understand that the involvement of an external substance in the internal processes of our brain is a serious violation of our natural balance, a balance that is most essential to our normal functioning.

Because it is so important that the working of the brain should not be interrupted by external factors, we are equipped with a special mechanism – a doorkeeper whose job it is to block such an influence. This mechanism is a sort of particularly dense membrane surrounding the brain and serves as a barrier against the intrusion of many kinds of substances. It is known as the Blood-Brain Barrier because the dense membrane prevents the passage of unwanted substances that might reach the brain through the blood stream.

However, psychoactive substances such as nicotine, as well as substances found in other drugs, penetrate this barrier without difficulty. The barrier doesn't spot these substances because their chemical composition sometimes resembles that of substances that the body itself produces. Thus the brain is unable to block their entrance, and their very presence within the system creates a new and very problematic balance of power.

REWARD AND CRAVING

At first, the presence of nicotine activates the brain's reward system which is the system responsible for feelings such as satisfaction, tranquility and security. However, the activation of this system in the brain by artificial means through the presence of nicotine actually causes the opposite effect. In order to explain how this happens it is important to first of all clarify the role of this system.

The term 'reward system' relates to good feelings which the brain is responsible for creating following actions that are beneficial to our bodily balance; for example, after eating, an act that contributes essential energy to our proper functioning; or rest and sleep that are essential to our feelings of alertness and concentration. This is also the case with physical exercise which benefits all the body's systems and helps to circulate oxygen to all its organs.

Our body requires all these things regularly. It is built in such a way that as long as we supply it with its requirements there is increased activity in the brain and the brain rewards us with a sense of wellbeing. In other words, our brains use the technique of producing good and pleasant feelings when we are in the right balance. Thus, from an early age we learn to recognize that eating, rest, and physical exercise, make us feel good.

We get such pleasant feelings not only as a result of our physical vitality. We also derive such sensations from pleasant smells such as that of flowers, listening to music or from the sense of excitement we feel when we see things that are esthetically pleasing and beautiful. In all sorts of situations which are beneficial to our balance – be it physical or mental – the brain reinforces the link between the situation and the feeling it creates. On the basis of this principle we get used to doing things that will activate this mechanism. In other words, we tend to do things that are simply good for us.

The 'reward system' does not operate in a vacuum. In matters that are related to good feelings in the physical sense it is, in effect, a response system. It functions as a balancing agent in relation to other processes whose role is precisely the opposite. These could be described as processes of craving or deficiency.

When our bodies experience a lack of something, our craving produces varying degrees of unease. That is what happens when we feel hungry, thirsty, tired, and so on. As the shortfall increases, so the feelings of unease grow. In such circumstances the body's sensors operate in order to transmit different messages between the brain cells which results in increased feelings of discomfort. In contrast to the operation of the reward system, what we now have is a craving that is responsible for linking situations in which there is a lack of some sort in the body to feelings of discomfort.

These two tendencies are expressed in our daily lives and the way in which we conduct ourselves. When we embark on a trip of several days and take with us food, drink, and other equipment, our supplies are planned in line with the patterns we have acquired as a result of our general experience of reward and craving.

On the one hand, we are well acquainted with the pleasant experiences of having meals in the bosom of nature. On the other hand, the unpleasant feelings resulting from a shortage of food and drink are also not alien to us. The variable activity between the brain cells operates as a factor that balances these feelings as necessary so that they influence our behavior accordingly.

This is a very sophisticated regulatory process of craving and reward of two sides that are opposites, when each of them is working in turn to achieve one objective. The objective – so far as every one of us is concerned – is to enable a stable life and the most efficient functioning possible of the body's systems. When we cover any sort of shortage, the reward system will create a calming effect and thus end the craving.

Why then is the artificial activation of the reward system, as a result of the stimulation created by nicotine not, in fact, a good thing? Since the body's reward system is a system of response its role is to function at the right time in order to bring to an end the craving and shortage in a natural way.

Feelings such as hunger, thirst, weakness, tiredness, pain and the like are supposed to disappear as we make sure that the shortages are filled. When the reward system is activated in an artificial way as a result of the intake of nicotine, it will result in feelings that are supposed to end a sense of unease that in reality doesn't actually exist.

Our brain notices this situation and accordingly tries to minimize the effect of the nicotine by means of a counter response. It achieves this by causing the brain cells to change themselves. It means a real change in the way the cells function so that they will be less affected by the excess artificial activity. As a result, the tolerance of the cells increases and they become less sensitive to the influences of the reward system.

The internal balance has been violated. On the one hand the reward system is unnecessarily stirred and activates the brain cells, while on the other hand the cells alter their way of functioning in order to moderate this excessive influence.

THE IMPACT OF DISTURBING THE BALANCE

The significant problem that this change produces surfaces at the point at which the nicotine we have consumed begins to vanish from our body. Nicotine is a fast acting substance and as such it also disperses within a short period of time. Approximately two hours after the smoking of a cigarette not much nicotine is left in the bloodstream, and just half an hour after smoking one can already feel a drop in the level of nicotine in the body. What happens as the nicotine leaves the body and its effect on the brain is lessened, is the major factor in causing the addiction to smoking and the creation of a constant physical need for cigarettes.

Following the departure of the nicotine the reward system, which had been needlessly activated by it, is no longer stimulated so that in a sense it returns to its normal state. However, since the cells have undergone a change, the lowered level of stimulation results in a rapid development of a feeling of craving.

We need to understand that over a long period of smoking we needlessly activate the reward system a number of times a day, as a result of which changes occur in our brain cells. The biggest change is that what was once our delicate chemical balance is in balance no more, and the only thing that will bring us back into balance is another intake of nicotine. But this is now a new balance.

We have created an upside-down reality. Instead of being OK when we are not in need of anything in particular, we only return to a feeling of balance when we re-introduce nicotine into our system. This leads to big differences in feelings between smokers and non-smokers. The smoker habituates his brain to demand an additional stimulus to properly arouse the reward system.

An excellent example to illustrate this change is familiar to all of us with the cigarette we smoke after a meal. Generally, smokers need to have a cigarette after eating. What is so special about this cigarette which smokers tend to regard as some sort of dessert? 'It's not the same without a cigarette' is what practically every smoker will tell you. For smokers this cigarette creates a feeling of relief, so much so that only after it does the smoker feel satiated. How does that work?

We have conditioned our brains to feel the influence of the reward system only when there has been an increase of the stimulus through an intake of nicotine. A non-smoker – which is what we all were in the past – needs nothing more than the natural arousal of the reward system that occurs after a meal. The natural processes in the brain stimulate the reward system and the brain cells immediately respond by creating a feeling of satiation.

However, so far as smokers are concerned, since we introduced the nicotine into our body systems, it requires us to supply a significantly greater level of activity than the brain produces naturally. The brain cells do not respond as they used to do, so that it becomes necessary to create a more powerful stimulus in order for us to feel satiated.

Of course the body will not do this of its accord and we therefore feel a kind of emptiness and a sense of craving. When we smoke a cigarette the nicotine begins once more to take effect and the cells, which are now in receipt of a sufficient level of stimulation, readily agree to create the feeling of satiation that we desire so much.

We have generated a state in which the preferable conditions given to us by nature have been diminished. We only return to some sort of balance if we continue to smoke cigarettes – a state the non-smoker achieves in a natural way. Many smokers simply don't understand how significant a matter this is.

By our very own actions we are changing our body's balance so that we can only feel good as long as we continue to 'fuel' ourselves up with more nicotine. As long as we experience a shortage of nicotine in our bodies we are immediately exposed to feelings of unease. As said earlier, after half an hour it is already possible to feel a decrease in the level of nicotine achieved following the last cigarette smoked.

Let's look for a moment at what 'to feel a drop in the level of nicotine' actually means? We gave an example that illustrates the extra stimulation required to create a feeling of satiation. But what about feelings of relaxation, restfulness, security, tranquility, pleasure and stability? All of these are linked to the influence of that same reward system so that without an increase in stimulation there will be a feeling of insufficiency in all these feelings as well.

The regular activity that the body creates in a natural way is not enough for us anymore, and that sadly is the reason why we feel pressured, tense and irritated when we are prevented from smoking in order to raise the level of nicotine in our body. The real reason for lighting additional cigarettes is in order to ease these unpleasant feelings. That is to say that cigarettes are not just needed in order for us to feel OK but that without a regular supply of nicotine we feel worse.

CHAPTER 5

A Unique Addiction

Like the addiction to every other drug, our addiction to nicotine makes us needy. The meaning of being a smoker is that I wake up every morning knowing that today, like every other day, I will have to smoke more cigarettes. It is part of my way of life, a reality over which I have no control. From this particular perspective, in a way that is similar to alcoholics and addicts to other drugs, smokers are addicted to nicotine.

Nevertheless, both as individuals and as a society we unconsciously ignore the addiction to nicotine. Nowadays, there is no other drug that we speak of as a 'habit'. It's become much less common to use the term 'he has an alcohol habit' or 'he has a heroin habit', whereas when it comes to nicotine it is common to say 'the smoking habit'. In all of these cases we are talking about the taking of a substance that affects the brain and disturbs our natural balance. In all cases when the usage is continuous the disturbance caused leads to the creation of a need and a dependence. And in all cases the addiction weakens the addicts both physically and mentally.

When the use of any drug leads to a visible behavioral change, the decrease in the addict's ability to function normally produces a clearly negative social response. Society does not tolerate the behavior of drunks and drugged up people and expects individuals to be in control of their actions and speech.

Accepted behavioral codes demand – and justifiably so – that we be sober and alert, since a society cannot function in an orderly way when people are not properly in control of their bodies or their ability to think clearly. People who are not fully in control of themselves are liable to be a danger to those around them as, for example, when driving under the influence of alcohol or when they are in a position of responsibility at work that demands supervision and vigilance.

IS IT JUST A HABIT?

The situation of the nicotine addict is very different indeed, of that there can be no doubt. Yet from a certain internal perspective there are some similarities. From an external perspective the situation of the smoker is certainly very different, as the substance does not affect the smoker's control over his body or the clarity of his thinking. Smokers don't feel a 'high' as a result of smoking, and generally get used to performing any task or piece of work while smoking.

This conceals the major reason for the mistaken tendency to regard smoking as a habit. When we see a drunk or a person high on drugs and are able to identify a change in his behavior, it is easy for us to notice that there has been a change for the worse in that person's control over his body, or his speech and the clarity of his thinking. We find it obvious to link the decrease in these faculties to the intake of some sort of substance.

Moreover, when someone is seen to be using such a substance continuously and sequentially while the same behavioral patterns are repeated, the logical diagnosis is that something in the substance has the power to compel the user to go on consuming it.

On the other hand, and contrary to the above, when non-smokers observe a smoker and don't see any change in his behavior and everything seems to be normal, they tend to classify his smoking as a habit. An improper habit, but nevertheless merely a habit.

When looking at it from the outside it doesn't seem logical to say that there is something in the substance the smoker is consuming that has the power to compel him to go on using it. Because when observed from the outside people don't notice any particular change, they mistakenly think that the smoker is fine with the cigarette and that he is simply 'used to it.' As a matter of fact, people don't even pay any special attention to this since smokers behave in a similar way when they are smoking and when they are not smoking. Accordingly, the observer has no grounds for categorizing the smoker's need to smoke as something that has a power over him.

When no behavioral change is visible, an observer would inevitably think that the smoker is in complete control. As a result, it very often happens that smokers are not properly understood by non-smokers, who expect them to behave like a person in control. Many smokers are asked 'why haven't you stopped already?' Such a question is not usually directed at someone who we think is not in full control and isn't himself able to bring about change. When the smoker replies 'you don't understand, I am really addicted to this' it is difficult for people to accept. If there is an addiction, if there is a force that has power over you, why isn't it outwardly visible?

So here is the point; there is an addiction and there is a force that has a power over smokers, but in this case the system works in a slightly opposite way. First of all the influence exerted by nicotine is, as we know, very subtle so no extreme behavioral change is expected. Indeed, if a change of any kind in the smoker's behavior is to be noticed it will actually be when the nicotine drug is not consumed rather than when it is.

It is actually when there is a shortage of nicotine in the blood that we become more irritable and stressed. The uniqueness of nicotine is that its effect is only felt when it is missing. When it is present in the bloodstream we do after all function properly. This means that it distorts the order of things so that when it is present in our system we feel in balance and when it is missing we are out of balance and feel unease.

And indeed, when is it really possible to observe the nicotine's power over the smoker? It is noticeable when the smoker is stuck without cigarettes or is forced to refrain from smoking for a prolonged period of time. At times like that we can sometimes see a smoker responding more aggressively than usual and appearing to be restlessness.

This process is defined as withdrawal symptoms, which is to say feelings of unease as a result of the withdrawal of nicotine from the body. Nevertheless, despite the unease, we are talking about a 'mild drug' and the withdrawal symptoms are not too severe.

Smoking cigarettes differs from the intake of other drugs in that while we are under the influence, meaning when we are 'smoked' all day, we function in a normal way and, in fact, the effect of the drug actually maintains our balance. The effect, so to speak, does not 'unbalance us' but rather keeps our balance.

So when is it that we feel that the balance has been disturbed? When there is a drop in the body's level of nicotine. When there is a shortage. In order to be OK we need to be 'smoked' all day. Outwardly, everything appears to be normal and is not perceived as an addiction. But inwardly we are addicted to smoking and it most definitely exerts a power over us.

EFFECT OVER TIME

Despite the fact that the immediate effect of each and every cigarette leads to no observable behavioral change, over time a significant change in our sensitivity to our surroundings does develop. Smokers tend to experience feelings of tension a number of times on any given day. Generally in our daily routine the feelings of tension are only slight. Such a condition is characterized by its consistency and doesn't get any special attention, especially since we make sure that we are in possession of our regular supply of cigarettes and make sure we take frequent smoking breaks.

Even so, the very fact that there is a regular sense of nagging or annoyance, forces our body system to deal with the experience of recurring tension. In nature these feelings of tension are not supposed to appear so frequently, and our bodies are not adjusted to deal with incessant harassment so often.

Therefore, through a constant process of adaptation, our thresholds of sensitivity change and, over time, we get used to living at a higher level of tension compared to a non-smoking person. If, for example, a door is slammed very noisily, we as smokers are liable to become more alarmed by such an incident than a non-smoker would be. We are more alert and more tensed up, and, over time and unintentionally, we tend to become more short-tempered.

This is so especially during those 'in between' periods when we are short of cigarettes or when we are lacking nicotine inside our bodies. It is difficult to maintain our very relaxed lifestyle when seething inside our bodies there are unbalanced feelings of craving and reward.

Sometimes during a working day I find myself travelling in a taxi in one or more busy and noisy city centers. Every time the way in which I am swept up by the stress and tension of taxi drivers who are smokers surprises me. Their restlessness is expressed in the way they react to what is happening around them on the roads. It is precisely from professional drivers like these that it would have been logical to expect level headedness and acceptance of the noisy traffic around them. After all, they have had plenty of experience of every likely situation – jams, honking of horns, illegal overtaking and many other possible circumstances. Nonetheless, it would seem that taxi drivers who smoke have a 'short fuse'. They are not the only ones. There are some non-professional drivers who smoke that are also short tempered. The body system becomes used to being on the alert at all times and over the years the reactions of smokers become increasingly impulsive.

Even though it is true that among smokers we can also find many who are able to be more tolerant and more patient, in most such cases this is linked to their individual ability to be outwardly restrained. But all smokers feel this incessant tension.

Most of us conduct ourselves in line with the demanding and fast moving lifestyle which typifies this era. Many of us do not manage to maintain a balanced lifestyle without any link to whether or not we are smokers. This is true of the diet we follow, the exercise we give our bodies, the mount of sleep we get, and so on. The additional restlessness that comes from the smoking of cigarettes wears us out and leads to us behaving even more rashly and hectically.

It's important that you should be aware that this point is actually a source of great optimism. Many who have stopped smoking have told me that one of the most substantial changes in their first period as non-smokers is expressed in the return of peace of mind and inner calm.

Our body is never ready to accept the ever recurring daily tension we experience as smokers. Therefore, within a very short period of time after we have stopped smoking, this continual state of tension is halted and is replaced by serenity and a state of stability.

Actually, we are not talking about some sort of spiritual vipassana insight and cosmic wellness but rather about the return of a fairly ordinary calm state. It's just that we as smokers have already managed to forget how pleasant it is to be without the intrusion of tension during the day.

For us this is not a usual state and it is a renewal that gets better and better in an early phase of our smoking cessation. The body is ready and willing to calm the systems and return to a life of balance. All that is required is to let it function in the way that it was designed to do by nature and stop burdening it with nicotine. And not only this; there is another process that happens to us which is encouraging; stopping to smoke opens the door to other significant changes in our lifestyle.

All of this is, of course, only relevant to those who quit smoking as a result of understanding the addiction and after proper preparation. However, when the opening to a satisfying and full life without cigarettes becomes available, there are many who find themselves amazed by the enormity of the change. They can barely believe how something that they thought was so powerful and so rooted within them can change almost effortlessly. How come that a reality that we were so sure that we could not manage without, suddenly appears to have no meaning for us?

Not only do we discover that it is indeed possible to do without that former reality, but also that the transition to a new state is swift and occurs without any difficulty. This great marvel may open the door to additional changes. Suddenly we want to make other adjustments in our lives and suddenly we feel that we are in control – that everything is in our hands.

At this stage, the above may not seem to you to be so realistic and that is understandable. Yet the simple truth is that all we need to do is to observe the processes that brought us to the place in which we now find ourselves. Nothing more than that is required of us.

The way out is directly related to the clarity of the understanding we gain of the addiction in both the physical as well as in the mental sense. There are no short cuts nor should there be any short cuts. In a very unique way, the more we look closely at the process happening to us in which cigarettes take control over our lives, the more, accordingly, will the process of setting free from smoking be shortened.

CHAPTER 6

The Transparent Enemy

The nicotine leaving our body feels to us like some sort of disturbance, a kind of unease. However, these processes are not given much attention because they seem to be happening to us behind the scenes, so to speak. One reason for this is that we tend to get relief by lighting another cigarette every time it bothers us and we begin to feel restless. We don't wait too long. As we see it, the cigarette we are about to smoke will, at least for the time being, make it easier, and that is enough. As long as we have restored nicotine to the body we don't need to be concerned. We have got used to buying time.

What's more, when we have no possibility of lighting up and the tension increases, whether that is because the pack has been emptied and we have to get new supplies – meaning go out and buy cigarettes – or whether it is because we are at a social event which requires us to hold on, the pressure to smoke preoccupies us to such an extent that our main thoughts revolve around the next cigarette. When we suffer in the present we have no motivation to think beyond a temporary solution. At first we tend to look for a short term solution to the immediate distress.

Another reason is that there are times when we might be very busy with some matter and our thoughts are so taken up with other things that for a while we simply don't feel any problem. One way or another, the reality that cannot be ignored is that whenever we refrain from smoking for a while, and assuming that we are also free to think about it, we cannot escape the feeling of a lack.

We have accustomed ourselves to live with a constant sense of shortage. However, when this shortage is filled by smoking or, alternatively, when our minds are diverted – when we are busy or focused on something or asleep – for a while we will not sense the shortage. But in the absence of one or other such factors, the fact is that in the periods between one cigarette and another we have sentenced ourselves to a permanent punishment of an empty feeling.

Nicotine's big act of deception is its ability to camouflage itself. In nature this is a substance that is colorless, a fact that possibly implies nicotine's most dangerous attribute. It is such a mild drug that it seems as if it doesn't really have an effect on us. We experience no sense of elation at the time we consume it and the only feeling we get is one of relieving, to an extent, the mild feelings of tension, unease, and irritability.

Since our dependency is created in a gradual process over time, we are not able to see that the tension and irritability are an outcome of a shortage of nicotine. Don't see? Like the substance itself, so the process of addiction is also transparent and therefore barely noticeable. So unnoticeable that we interpret the reality as the opposite of what it really is. We tend to think that the tension and perpetual feeling of agitation are a result of the difficulties we encounter in our regular lives.

Ever so quietly, one step at a time, our body becomes used to getting doses of nicotine every day. Slowly, slowly, an internal need is born which we don't notice. No wonder then that when that need becomes well rooted, many of us don't understand it because we didn't notice it happening.

The changes in our natural balance described earlier, mainly serve to strengthen the processes of craving. With cigarettes we don't experience a substantial effect in contrast to what is usually experienced with other drugs or alcohol. That is precisely the reason that people don't usually at all relate to nicotine as a drug either in legal terms or in social terms.

Professionals tend not to incorporate it within the list of drugs which it is a priority for addicts to stop using, saying that 'it doesn't alter a person's consciousness.' Meaning that it doesn't get you drunk, nor does it blur one's thinking or produce a 'high'. At most it slightly raises the heartbeat and somewhat lifts the level of alertness. And if society and professional people underestimate it why should smokers think any differently?

SELF-DECEPTION

We are deceived into thinking that our craving to smoke stems from the difficulties in our regular lives, whereas the real reason is that we are addicted to a drug the lack of which in our blood stream is the source of our craving. In fact, the nicotine that leaves our body after the last cigarette was smoked is solely responsible for creating the physical craving for the next cigarette.

Moreover, we again fall into a trap when we perceive the next cigarette as the one that will ease the tension – for the simple reason that it does indeed give us a feeling of temporary relief.

Because we are unaware of the actual reality taking place in our bodies we disregard the previous cigarette and ignore the significant fact that our body is sending us signals of distress every time the presence of nicotine within us begins to diminish. We regard our condition as normal and it just seems to us that a number of times a day, as the level of tension rises a bit, all we have to do is to smoke the next cigarette. It doesn't occur to us that such a reality is not natural for human beings and that among non-smokers the daily level of tension doesn't at all rise with the frequency that it does among smokers.

I sometimes meet smokers in our cessation program who have become so used to this daily state that they admit that it seems strange to them that non-smokers never ask for a cigarette, even when they are anxious and under pressure. Just look at how much some of us twist the reality: Instead of realizing that there is a pattern here that is unnatural and that it is an outcome of us being smokers, we relate to our condition as if everything was in order, and as if it was perfectly natural for us to be in need from time to time of relief in the form of smoking the next cigarette.

Sadly, this relief is felt because of our chemical imbalance – which is a direct outcome of our addiction to nicotine. A cigarette offers no real help to us in dealing with the tension and difficulties in our lives. All it does is to ease an additional problem that stems exclusively from smoking itself – from us being smokers.

ALTERING CONSCIOUSNESS

We are told that nicotine doesn't alter our consciousness. Well, it most certainly does. I remember this very well from the time when I too was a smoker, and I encounter this phenomenon still now in relation to participants in our meetings. Our addiction to cigarettes intimidates us. It weakens us so much that when it comes to smoking we sometimes behave disproportionately.

We find ourselves holding a cigarette in all sorts of different situations in our lives: during a phone call, in the street, in a coffee shop, at a meeting, before a flight, immediately after a flight, after exercising, after sleeping, and so on. It is only logical that we would try and smoke whenever possible. Whenever the body lacks nicotine, the feelings of craving and unease are there all the time. We have already forgotten what freedom feels like, what it is to be in real control of our lives.

A participant in one of our meetings once said to me: 'I need a cigarette when facing up to someone or when I am having an argument.' 'And what, without the cigarette you are unable to do that?' I asked. 'I don't feel confident, I blush' he replied.

Instead of understanding that they descend to such a weak level where they cannot even have a conversation with someone without holding a lit cigarette in their hand, many smokers will try and explain, both to themselves and to others, that cigarettes really help on such occasions.

If that was really the case, we could shove a cigarette into a non-smoker's hand and say: 'Take it. It will help you when dealing with other people.' Were we to do such a thing the non-smoker would regard us as nothing short of crazy. In his perception smokers are holding on to something that has no connection to reality. Accordingly he will ask: 'How can this repulsive thing, the size of an ear swab, that burns at one end and produces plumes of suffocating and unpleasant smoke, possibly help me with anything?'

It may surprise you to know, but I have more than once come across smokers who really believed that non-smokers are jealous of them. When looking more deeply into the basis for such a perception, we come to the conclusion that our natural tendency as human beings is to always interpret the reality from the perspective of our own personal viewpoint.

Our unconscious might be saying to us 'if you feel that you need this, then for sure the other person also feels the same.' Only when we stop and think in a conscious way what the person facing us is thinking – referring to his point of view – does it become easier to notice the differences between our perceptions and theirs. But the natural tendency in our daily lives is to apply our thinking patterns to the other person as well.

Drugs that alter our consciousness are classified as such when they lead us to experience instant change. This refers to an experience that is characterized by a significant effect on our functioning. However, the process by which cigarettes alter our consciousness occurs in a different way and there is no significant outward sign of the change at all.

People don't look at you and say 'look at how smoked this person is', in contrast to what they would say about a person who is drunk or someone who is drugged. Nevertheless, the process influencing our perceptions is reinforced every day. The assumption in our conscious mind that without cigarettes we are helpless and weak becomes more and more ingrained all the time. And this is most certainly a consciousness altering change.

CHAPTER 7

The Addiction Experience

We are continuing to explore differing perspectives of our addiction to smoking. These are the tools we have to acquire in order to become free at a later stage. Even though you might not feel it just now, this observation and the understanding we are now getting of the factors that constitute our addiction, create an internal process that prepares us for change.

Don't be preoccupied now with the thoughts of actually stopping to smoke, they are not relevant at this stage. Now it is much more important to become familiar with the addiction itself and the place it occupies in our lives. We are now building stable foundations of understanding and awareness, and these foundations will, later on, enable us to become smokefree from a position of strength and control.

Generally, smoking for a daily smoker is not experienced as a choice but as a need. In our day to day experience, smoking does not differ very much from our need to eat and drink and all our other needs. This recognition should make things somewhat easier for us as there's no room for developing too many guilty feelings about our inability to stop smoking.

We didn't become addicted to smoking as a result of a firm and conscious decision that once we started we wouldn't be able to break free from it in the future. On the contrary, we took this risk when we began to smoke because we didn't at all believe that there was any chance of our becoming addicted. We had come across addicted smokers and heard them warn us not to begin smoking. However, in exactly the same way as the non-smoking public looks at us today and regards smoking as merely a habit, so too did we look upon smokers before we began. We failed to realize that there is a real but imperceptible risk of addiction.

Even though everyone in fact notices that among smokers there is a certain need to smoke, yet non-smokers don't really understand the concept of addiction as it relates to the smoking of cigarettes. From the perspective of the non-smoker, the smoker is viewed as someone acting in a way that outwardly appears to be entirely an act of free choice. In the main this is because no behavioral change in the smoker can be seen when comparing the period prior to his smoking with the period during which he is smoking, or the period after which he has finished to smoke.

There isn't a day that passes without a non-smoker saying to a smoker 'Well, when are you going to stop smoking?' as if the smoker wasn't at all aware of the problem and only this reminder was required to wake him up. As if it was as simple as that. This is also the way that most of us saw things at the time when we didn't smoke and it seemed to us that we could have a bit of fun by smoking and drop it whenever we wanted to.

It can be said with certainty that for almost all smokers the addiction is an outcome of a failure to recognize the risk involved. It is hardly possible to imagine someone beginning to smoke if, from the outset, they had understood the addiction as it is perceived by the average smoker in his daily experience, or at least understood in advance the significance of the restricted and anguished life lead by an addict.

The very word 'addicted' includes the idea that the person has lost his independence. In the past, human trafficking was an acceptable trade and people were sold into slavery and servitude. The person sold into slavery lost his independence and was forced to work for his master. The working and living conditions of the slave were determined by the master to whom he was sold.

In today's world, forced labor is unacceptable in all civilized societies and yet an addiction to a variety of things is known. From a societal perspective the addiction to cigarettes is at the top of the list. The cigarette addict enslaves himself to nicotine and pays a very high price for it. In addition to food and beverage he must consume yet another product. He has to create additional income or cut down on his regular outgoings in order to finance the purchase of cigarettes. He loses his independence and the natural sense of freedom in daily life, and has to also pay for it in the form of various health related and social costs well known to us all.

SMOKING AT ADOLESCENCE

Paradoxically, this process which we began in order to cross boundaries and feel liberated is, in fact, the very process that enslaves us and hems us in. More than ninety percent of smokers begin their smoking career in their teens – the age of adolescence. During this period most of us shape our identity as adults and undergo a process of becoming independent. A part of this process includes experimentation and the crossing of boundaries. To a large extent this occurs in areas that are perceived as a line marking the difference between kids and adults.

As children we view smoking as an act that belongs to the world of grown-ups. In adolescence the natural tendency is to connect ourselves to this adult world because adolescents want to be part of it. It is part of the process of shaping our independent entity. That world symbolizes independence and freedoms in the sense that an adult is his own master as opposed to a child who is bound by the authority of his parents and has limited autonomy in the making of decisions that affect him.

The transition to the adult world is not something that attracts youngsters because of the increased level of responsibility that an adult has to bear. In fact, so far as the adolescent is concerned, that aspect doesn't count for much, and young people tend not to think about it. What motivates the young is the wish to free themselves from the restrictions and limitations of childhood. The entire concept of youthful rebellion stems from the adolescent's internal feeling that he is already big enough, thoughtful enough, and experienced enough, for people to relate to him as such, and allow him to begin to conduct his life the way he wants to – exactly as is done in the adult world.

The physical and social changes that adolescents go through leads to a response that is expressed in behavioral changes. These changes are increasingly revalidated as they become more noticeable. In this context cigarettes are likely to play an important role in giving the adolescent a feeling of adulthood.

Only adults smoke cigarettes and it is not the business of children. They are bitter, they make your throat sore, and there is something harsh about them which you need to overcome in order to tolerate them.

Cigarettes arouse outward responses that in part do not flatter the adolescent. This set of responses clearly confirms that the message of the adolescent is being transmitted, the message that he is now a person able to make independent decisions whether others like it or not.

The actual process of learning how to smoke correctly, holding the cigarette in a proper way and inhaling as one is supposed to, becomes a kind of rite of passage.

AN ADDICTION THAT DOESN'T GO AWAY

This reality could have been considered to be reasonable if the phenomenon of smoking – as an indication of adolescence – would, like all the other characteristics of that particular period of life, come and then go. The sad fact is, however, that whereas all the other changes and customs of adolescence do indeed pass into history, the addiction to smoking remains. This happens both because of the physical addiction to nicotine that doesn't let go of the smoker, and also because of the weakening that occurs in the smoker's self-image.

At the beginning, the self-confidence of the novice is somewhat enhanced when he starts to smoke in company. Indeed, there are many social situations in which youngsters are able to feel more loosened up and more self-confident when holding a cigarette. But in time a dependency on cigarettes develops as does the self-image they create for the adolescent.

Subsequently there is a continual weakening until the smoker is almost unable to manage in social situations without the aid of cigarettes, and certainly unable to feel self-confident without them.

Thus cigarettes, which at first signify for youngsters their personal independence and their liberation from the restrictions of childhood and early youth, quickly turn into a reality of distressing addiction. The clearest indication of this is the enslavement to smoking that takes place, and the smoker's inability to change this pattern of behavior.

I am sometimes asked to assist people who have only been smoking for a few months, to quit. What surprises me in such cases is not how quickly they get addicted – something that seems to take hold of the freshman smoker towards the end of just one month of smoking – but rather the awareness of these young smokers as to their condition and their desire to find a way out.

Such youngsters represent a very small minority. In most cases, smokers tend to avoid dealing with the reality of their addiction until they have smoked for a number of years. The tendency is to regard the existing situation as a matter of free will without acknowledging that this is not really a matter of will but rather a situation in which there is no choice. A smoker who would like to test this has to simply decide to refrain from smoking for a significant period, let's say a month, and see whether he finds it difficult, or is at all able to implement that decision. In most cases young smokers are unwilling to even try this for just a few days.

A more serious matter is that they convince themselves that this is certainly a decision made of their own free will. The most common excuse is that there is simply no reason to waste their energy on that at this stage. The sentence usually trotted out is that 'when the time comes and I'm fed up with it, I'll stop smoking.' Simple and easy. This perception is a clear expression of the wishful thinking of virtually every smoker namely, that one day he will simply be 'fed up' of smoking and just won't want to do it anymore without making any effort or having symptoms of any kind.

Since this doesn't happen 'just like that', it is unrealistic for the smoker to wait in vain for the addiction to somehow just disappear. The passage of time only serves to reinforce the addiction and certainly doesn't weaken it.

CHAPTER 8

Light Smokers

There are many smokers who are constrained by the structure of their lives to refrain from smoking for many hours during the day. In this day and age this is a very common occurrence since in many countries smoking is prohibited in a wide range of places. Numerous smokers are prevented from smoking in their workplace, in commercial centers, in homes where there are children, in shops, and so on. Such smokers sometimes unwillingly become lighter smokers in terms of the number of cigarettes they consume.

Some other smokers actually force themselves to refrain from smoking for various reasons and do so even though nobody is placing a restriction on them. Additionally, there are cases of people who, for medical reasons and difficulties in breathing, or for financial reasons, are limited in their consumption capacity.

Such smokers, whose daily consumption is smaller, may misunderstand what we described earlier on. Some of them are likely to think that they have some sort of control over their smoking addiction. The source of this mistake lies in the thought that a reduction in the amount actually smoked affects the extent of the addiction and the strength of the dependency on cigarettes.

So as to be clear, it is important to point out that this restraint in no way conflicts with the processes described here. The way we refer to the addiction to cigarettes focuses on processes that are inevitable.

As a result of the effect of nicotine on our bodies, cigarettes reinforce the processes of craving among all smokers regardless of whether they are heavy or light smokers. Inevitably, feelings of shortage and unease are created. Moreover, among all smokers this craving can be temporarily eased by the smoking of a cigarette that supplies the smoker with an additional dose of nicotine. These are processes that occur among all smokers without exception.

Despite the fact that there are smokers who are forced to abstain from smoking for extended periods, this limitation doesn't in any way alter the fact that the craving continues. It also doesn't alter the fact that when smokers think about a cigarette – whether they refrain from smoking because of an externally imposed restriction or impose that restriction on themselves – they indeed feel a need to smoke.

The difference between smokers mainly lies in the way they cope with this abstention. There are many who learn to live with the limitation and come to terms with it relatively easily. There are others who suffer more and struggle against it. Either way, one thing is clear; the craving to smoke is common to all.

This craving is noticeable at different times and in various situations. For example, after a long flight both light and heavy smokers will feel the pressure to smoke. From the perspective of the lighter smokers, enough time has elapsed since the last cigarette for them to legitimately smoke again. So it will be in many other situations in which they have refrained from smoking for a lengthy period of time.

Light smokers are not necessarily 'light addicts'. Indeed their addiction is sometimes very frustrating. At one level or another, people who smoke daily, including those who are regarded as light smokers, experience a dependency on cigarettes.

Many light smokers who refrain from smoking by restraining themselves, designate certain fixed times during the day for smoking. They take breaks at certain specific times: have a cigarette in the morning in order to accelerate their digestive system, have a cigarette after a big meal, and so on. They try to attribute certain roles to the cigarettes they smoke and are not prepared to smoke just like that. Among such smokers cigarettes are promoted in rank and assigned roles. Accordingly, the dependency on these cigarettes is increased.

Light smokers often wonder why they are unable to quit completely. They look at heavy smokers who smoke large quantities without counting, and it seems to them that the fact that they smoke significantly less confirms that they are actually less addicted. As a result they think that it should be easier for them to stop smoking altogether.

The reality is rather different. A light smoker can actually be a 'heavy addict' because he develops a tendency to over value every cigarette. Despite the reduced quantity, the attention paid to the cigarettes is increased. A light smoker who smokes daily has to deal time and again with the question of whether to smoke now or wait. This continuous conscious thinking and the calculation of how much time has elapsed between one cigarette and another overly preoccupies such a smoker.

This is a 'pleasure' that heavier smokers have let go of at the price of an increase in the amount smoked. That at least has saved the heavier smokers from having to deal with this unending struggle, and releases them from having to answer irritating questions such as 'how many have I smoked today?'; 'Does my daily intake allow me to smoke more than I already have?'; 'Have I smoked too many today?' Heavy smokers more or less know what their daily average is and this assessment doesn't involve any special effort on their part.

All of us, including those who are considered light smokers, have better days and days that are less good. On less good days, days of pressure and increased tension, all smokers will smoke more regardless of the daily intake they are used to. After such a day the smoker who, for example, is used to smoking five a day, will find that he has finished almost a whole pack. Usually, that smoker will be very frustrated by this.

It is also possible that from a physical point of view he won't feel well as a result of the increase in the amount of smoke his body has had to absorb beyond the level it is accustomed to.

Light smokers tend to be angry with themselves after days like this. The descent into smoking double or even more than double the usual amount does not square with the general assumption that they are in control of the situation. And this is really the main point – daily light smokers don't have any real control over the addiction. They do attempt more actively to struggle against the effects of nicotine and the craving that it creates. These attempts are bound to fail time and again as a consequence of changes in the daily routine due to specific tensions and unforeseen days of greater than usual pressure.

Bit by bit, as the years go by, many light smokers become heavier smokers. As the number of days on which a light smoker consumes a 'larger than usual' quantity mount up, the motivation to struggle against this need and the continuous craving, weakens.

It has to be understood that all smokers go through a similar process. No smoker gets used to smoking an entire pack a day within a short period of time. The process of addiction inevitably involves a phase during which the smoker is defined as being a light smoker. During that period he is able to console himself to an extent by the reassurance that he has at least not descended to the level of the heavy smokers.

At the end of the day, most smokers do not remain light smokers and end up consuming close to a pack a day and even more. A small proportion of smokers though, do continue to smoke a lesser amount. However, the message to the lighter smokers among us – or those among us who are still regarded as light smokers – is this: It is essential that you recognize the true reality which is that a lower consumption does not in any way reflect a control over the addiction.

CHAPTER 9

Physical Disturbance

There are many ways in which this weakening affects us. Our body systems are no longer in the balance they once were, and our state of the art 'space vehicle' has to deal on a daily basis with an intake of smoke that contains a few thousand different sorts of chemicals.

This means that our various physical systems are overburdened. This overburdening diminishes the vitality of the organs and their various functions. Everything gets used to working differently – performing under overload conditions. The smoke interferes with the processes of circulating oxygen to the various organs, which also means that less oxygen reaches the organ that needs it most – the brain.

This burden, together with the fact that the texture of our blood becomes thicker, forces the heart to also work harder. Excessive effort by our systems necessitates changes in the body's overall balance. The digestive system works differently and the speed of the body's metabolism is also altered. The lungs, which absorb a major part of the smoke, also have difficulty functioning in the way they did in the past.

If we were to describe smoking as an attack on our body system by a hostile military force, we could say that the lungs are on the front line and absorb the main barrage of fire. Were it not for their stubborn struggle against the incoming smoke, a far greater number of harmful substances would penetrate our bodies. And indeed, just as it is in war, so too in this battle, all the systems are mobilized to help in trying to overcome the aggressors.

Such phenomena as coughing and phlegm are good examples illustrating the way in which the body drives out some of the harmful intruders. This unending struggle is quite complicated and interesting. The buildup of phlegm and the need to cough are things we are familiar with often after a night's sleep. It is also common among some of those who have quit smoking, in the early days after they stop. The body takes advantage of the lull in smoking due to sleep or an abstention due to some other reason. These pauses are a kind of cease-fire which the body immediately uses as an opportunity to drain the poisonous substances within by bringing up phlegm and coughing, or both. Some who have quit describe this process as lasting a few days. It is actually a good sign indicating the beginning of an adjustment to a new setting. The body is signaling to us that it now has the time to work more intensively to cleanse whatever it can.

GETTING ADDICTED BENEATH THE WARNING SYSTEMS

Our bodies function in a fascinating way not only when all is well but also even when they are under constant external attack. Every night while we are asleep, and on every other occasion when we don't smoke, our physical systems make a continuous effort to protect themselves against the effects of smoking.

In any event, this Sisyphean struggle also has a price tag. Among the ways in which our enfeeblement is expressed is by an increased vulnerability to illnesses. We become more vulnerable because our body is very preoccupied in dealing with a constant attack by smoke and poisons. Here too we can see that the most dangerous enemy is the one that is able to hurt us quietly while we pay no attention.

Despite the fact that this enemy seriously weakens us over time, when it comes to our day to day functioning we don't actually feel it. The reason for this is that smoking weakens us slowly and gradually. If, when we started smoking we were in good physical shape, then it will necessarily take several months before we are able to suddenly notice that there has been a deterioration in our physical fitness. In reality, due to our smoking this deterioration has been taking place daily. Yet the extent of the day by day decline in our fitness is very small.

When changes occur in small steps we don't notice them that much. The overall feeling we have is that one day is very much the same as the day before. In line with this process the addiction to cigarettes is reinforced step by step, day after day. When beginning to smoke cigarettes, no smoker expects that he will become addicted to them. As for the addiction, the feeling always is that after a period of smoking we suddenly find ourselves hooked and unable to stop.

The amazing sophistication lies in the fact that our warning systems are not turned on to alert us to the danger of our becoming addicted to cigarettes. A person who, for example, has drunk himself into a stupor, pays a price for this in the loss of self-control and possibly waking up with a hangover. The body of a person unused to a regular intake of alcohol also has to deal with an 'attack' by external forces that affect his balance and normal functioning.

At first sight it would seem that this resembles the experience of a smoker. But the big difference is that in the case of getting drunk the impact is very much felt and the change in the ability to function is highly noticeable.

Alcohol affects a number of things including reducing our concentration, impairing our motor capacity, and weakening our visual focus. A person who has been drinking will sometimes find it difficult to walk steadily and may also feel dizzy and tired.

On the morning after the night before, many who have drunk to excess have to cope with the unpleasant experience of a hangover. The body has suffered a shake-up of some kind and its warning systems are activated. There are symptoms that include a headache, tiredness, nausea and others. The body is giving out signals of an invasion on the previous day by an undesirable enemy, and that in future it would be best to avoid getting into such situations.

Moreover, on the assumption that the behavior of the drunk was in some way embarrassing, there can sometimes be psychological consequences in the form of feelings of disgrace and guilt. Such feelings also stir the drinker to examine his actions and think about what has happened.

This unpleasant experience serves as a pointer to the future and an indicator of his limitations. Were we to endure similar experiences after smoking an average of a pack, it is very reasonable to assume that most of us would never become addicted.

DON'T COUNT THE CIGARETTES

There exists a widespread problem of smoking and excessive drinking by youngsters. More often than not it is the young who are in danger of drinking more than they should. When it comes to alcohol they are inexperienced and unable to predict the amount that will in fact get them drunk. Many youngsters do indeed get drunk and experience the symptoms linked to that condition.

Fortunately, in most societies this phenomenon has no long term consequences. It is highly unlikely that youngsters will become addicted to alcohol as a result of excessive drinking at parties or during holidays. Particularly those who drank too much and as a result experienced unpleasant physical or mental side effects, or both, are likely to distance themselves from alcohol.

Yet, there are youngsters who, from approximately the age of twelve and above, start to smoke cigarettes for the first time in their lives at parties or some such event. Those first cigarettes are not so pleasant for the beginner. Their bitter taste, the strong smell, and the sense that they are going to choke, make every new smoker cough, feel dizzy and react in other such ways.

Nevertheless, the first few cigarettes don't have to be inhaled all the way into the lungs, and the main thing about smoking at this stage is about self-image. This experience is linked to a perception suggesting that a person holding a cigarette in his hand feels more 'grown up'.

Unlike drinking strong spirits for the first time, the first cigarettes do not cause any form of insobriety, do not affect the motoring skills of the smoker, and do not make it difficult for him to walk steadily, or interfere with his sight or his ability to talk coherently. They are regarded as nothing more than a façade.

For beginners, just holding a cigarette is part of a rite of passage. And because of that, precisely because those first cigarettes do not leave the mark of a powerful experience, it leads youngsters to continue to smoke long after the parties and the holidays have ended. It is more accurate to say that it is after these events that they become smokers.

Like everyone else, at the beginning they become light smokers and their smoking mostly takes place in social situations. However, after a not very long period of time, they begin to consume cigarettes as part of their regular life. Welcome to the next generation of the tobacco companies' submissive servants. Many smokers who come to our meetings report that they began their smoking career in the frivolous atmosphere at parties and holidays during their youth.

Just think of the wastage, the money, the harm to health, the squandering of time, bad odors, enslavement, self-deception and the like, which these freshman smokers are going to experience. Even heavy smokers, or perhaps we should say that heavy smokers in particular, tend to tell these youngsters 'don't start with this; you are entering a world that will imprison you.' And yet this doesn't prevent a single youth from starting.

There is nothing to be done – your actions say more about you than does anything else. Youngsters learn by observing the behavior of their elders not from what those elders say to them, certainly not when they say one thing and do another. The sincerity of what the adult says is not what impresses the youngster, and to a certain extent justifiably so. When someone urges you to behave in a certain way while at the same time they themselves behave in an entirely different way, the advice is unconvincing.

For youngsters, the sermonizer's admission of his own addiction doesn't really change anything because they still don't understand the meaning of this concept. However regrettable as it may be, by the time they do understand as a result of their own personal experience, it will be a bit too late. By that time they themselves will have become addicts.

CHAPTER 10

Interrupting the Natural Balance

So far we have focused on observing the human body's natural systems and the predominant influence of smoking on the way in which we function. This observation leads to a clear distinction between two optional paths in life. My preferred way of presenting these two paths is by an analogy between the cosmic behavior of the earth and that of the human structure.

In ancient folklore earth is regarded as a kind of 'big world' whereas man is regarded as a 'small world'. Accordingly, the range of processes that occur in the 'big world' have their parallel in the 'small world'. For the purposes of our examination, the point to focus on is the harmony that can be seen in the natural behavior of these two worlds.

The earth, a celestial body, is at all times in motion and in balanced symmetry with other celestial bodies such as the sun and the moon. The earth spins around its own axis making an entire rotation once every day and it revolves around the sun and completes a full orbit every three hundred and sixty five days and a bit – that is to say once a year.

This reality is cyclical and consistent, and the permanent orbit makes life on earth as we know it possible. In particular this pattern reflects a delicate balance which enables ordinary life to exist, and in fact it could be said that this is actually what makes life itself possible altogether. Today we know that if the earth was slightly closer to the sun or slightly further away from it, life on earth would not be viable. Because if that was so, the temperatures on earth would either be too high for life to be sustained or, alternatively, the earth would be completely frozen. This reality represents a strict harmony between the celestial bodies, enabling the optimal conditions for the existence of life.

In line with this phenomenon there are also natural processes taking place within our bodies aiming to maintain a correct and harmonious balance. This both within the body itself as well as in relation to our external surroundings.

In a remarkable way no less precise than that which occurs in the solar system, our human body maintains itself in balance and adjusts to the various needs and varying conditions so as to allow us to live in the most optimal way. The processes of life which are embedded within us make our physical systems work in a pre-determined way to ensure our natural balance. Just as in the 'big world' so in our 'small world' there are physical states of reward and craving that may resemble high and low tides, tiredness and wakefulness as opposed to night and day, and so on.

During sessions, I have become used to presenting two drawings on the white board, one beneath the other. In the upper drawing there is a large circle representing the sun. Next to the sun I draw a much smaller circle with a number of patches in it that represent the earth. The patches are, of course, the earth's continents. A line extends out from the earth that orbits the sun, disappears behind it, and then returns to the smaller circle – the earth. This line represents the symmetrical and smooth orbit followed by earth in its annual journey around the sun.

In the lower image I show exactly the same drawing except that the line representing earth's orbit isn't depicted as a smooth line, but rather as a line that has ups and downs resembling the graphs of share indices traded on the stock exchange. It is a line with evident fluctuations.

These drawings illustrate two options that are open to us in our human reality. If we look at it from the perspective of the 'natural way' our path as humans corresponds to the upper drawing. Just as the earth spins around its own axis and revolves around the sun in a uniform and smooth way, so too our path in life is meant to be conducted. The human body is fashioned perfectly so that it functions properly without hitches or disturbances.

But we also have the option to conduct our lives along a path that resembles the lower drawing, a path that is neither symmetric nor harmonious and is prone to frequent hitches and disturbances. Such a path represents fairly well what happens to us as smokers. Our daily lives are filled with disturbances and feelings of unease that push us to take cigarette breaks. Our bodies are required to make an excessive effort in order to cope with the smoke and nicotine and still function properly. This results in increased levels of tiredness, sluggishness and a weakening of our immune systems. We deal less well with illnesses and erode our blood vessels, lungs and heart more intensely.

Our body has a natural tendency to follow the path in the upper drawing which I have described. What prevents it from a normal and smooth daily course is the burden we impose on it as smokers. It is very important that we focus on this reality. We possess a system that is just perfect, an outstanding space vehicle, and all we have to do in order for it to function optimally – enabling us to enjoy our lives in the best way possible – is to ensure that we don't damage it with unnecessary nicotine and smoke; that we don't cause it to descend to the lower path.

CHOOSING THE RIGHT PATH

The distinction between these two paths in life which I have described is of the utmost importance. It has no practical implication at this stage because we have not yet dealt with the issue of the tools we need to acquire, and the route we will need to follow in order to shift away from the life depicted in the lower drawing to the one in the upper drawing.

What is important at this stage is that we sit down with ourselves and carefully consider which path we would really like to be on. The process we have gone through so far was not intended to convince you that it is preferable to be on the upper path, since that is obvious. Rather, what we have done is to open up a new horizon regarding our reality as smokers.

Since virtually all of us have, at some point, found ourselves stuck with the fact that we are addicted to smoking, we have now uncovered a broad explanation as to how this happened and how it works on us on a daily basis. Information and details that we were unaware of now become a great deal clearer and enable us, perhaps for the first time, to realize the true meaning of our being smokers.

Whoever chooses to exit the smoking cycle and get on the right and natural track of life needs to do no more than to read on. You are going to acquire the knowledge and the tools with which to cross over to this track efficiently and rapidly.

And whoever chooses to remain on the unnatural track will also gain something from the process we have gone through. That is because for the first time since the beginning of his smoking career he has the real option to choose this reality rather than to be dragged into it without understanding how it evolved. If among us there are some who prefer to remain loyal customers of the tobacco companies, they will at least from now on be customers who make a conscious choice and not simply allow themselves to be drawn into this situation.

It is important to emphasize once again that I don't expect any one of you to take any practical action on the basis of this knowledge. You don't yet have all of the required background and the tools to shift to the upper path. But you do have the option of making a firm decision about which path you would prefer to live your life on regardless of whether you get there or not.

And you will indeed get there – much more quickly and easily that seems possible to you just now. It is a tremendously important decision because when you set out on a new path the distinction between the path that you are leaving behind and the path that you want to reach will be constantly in your sights. That is the reason why I prefer to clarify these matters by using the analogy between the two possible paths.

By the way, for some reason the tobacco companies do not want you to know and understand the processes that someone who starts to smoke goes through and how the dependency on cigarettes evolves. For some reason the tobacco companies are not interested in customers that have a good understanding of what they are getting themselves into when they take their first steps in smoking.

And no wonder! We are being sold a harmful product that damages the quality of our lives – a product whose capacity to remain on the shop shelves is entirely dependent on the user's addiction. Clearly then, it is preferable that the consumer should not know this information in advance or even know it at all.

The cigarette companies understand very well that anyone who sooner or later becomes aware of the life course he is being dragged into by smoking will want to change his condition. They rely on the fact that most of their customers will only get to understand that they are addicted and are paying a high price for that physically, mentally, and economically, at as late a stage as possible. By then most smokers will be weak and will have come to terms with the reality of being addicted.

It is no wonder that it took several decades before the cigarette companies were forced to admit that the products they were selling are indeed addictive. Despite the unambiguous scientific research in their possession for many years which clearly pointed to cigarettes as being addictive and the cause of diseases, they never bothered to inform the public of this. To do so would have been equal to cutting off the branch they are sitting on.

Part Two:
The Mental Effect

CHAPTER 1

The Psychological relation to Smoking

The physical addiction to nicotine is not, in fact, our major problem as smokers. Though the physical addiction creates a constant urge to consume more and more cigarettes, the real strength of the addiction is embedded in our emotions and ways of thinking. If these matters could be separated I might possibly have started the book with a review of our psychological relation to smoking. But it is the feelings of physical craving and our mental perceptions that are jointly responsible for creating the grip that cigarettes have over us. These two are linked and one arouses the other. In other words, in our daily lives what pushes us to smoke is the feeling of a physical lack of some sort, as well as the thought that is aroused in the wake of that feeling which says to us 'I need a cigarette.'

Basically our mental system consists entirely of the intellectual and emotional functions that we use during our lives. These are our thoughts and feelings in relation to the reality surrounding us. In a way that is similar to the ongoing process of the physical addiction to nicotine, we undergo a psychological process during our lives as smokers. This process leads to a real change in the way in which we define ourselves.

If at the beginning of our path as smokers we perceived ourselves as being non-smokers who were simply experimenting with the smoking experience, by now we have already come to terms with defining ourselves as 'smokers'. This can be seen when we enter a restaurant or bar and the waiter asks 'smoking or non-smoking?' so as to know where to seat us. There can be no doubt that so long as it is solely up to us to decide, the clear answer will be 'smoking please.'

We are reminded of this tagging in a range of situations as, for example, when we meet a new partner, or are looking for a roommate; every time we are in the company of non-smokers and have to ask permission to smoke or apologize for having to go out for a cigarette break; the long journey to the smoke filled room at the airport; every day when we return to our regular shop to buy a new pack. In an enormous number of situations in our lives we get reminders that reinforce our personal definition 'I am a smoker'.

From time to time we get the chance to sit down with another smoker or a number of smokers, and discuss our socially difficult situation. How restricted we are, and how rudely non-smokers sometimes relate to us as if we had become the public's enemy. Occasionally at such meetings we speak with great nostalgia about how it used to be possible to smoke everywhere and especially during flights. Over the past few years, that once large number of options has been greatly reduced and there are some places in the world, such as New York City, that have taken far reaching steps which even prevent people from smoking on beaches and in parks, open spaces in every sense of the word.

As an ex-smoker, and as someone who is in constant contact with smokers, it is important for me to say that I fully empathize with the hardship that this leads to. We can debate at length the importance of educating youngsters not to start smoking, and we can also discuss the enormous advantages of quitting. However, when we are dealing with the actual situation as opposed to what is desirable, we cannot ignore the fact that there are people who need to smoke quite a few times a day and that forcing them to refrain undermines them and the quality of their lives, in the way they experience life as smokers. A smoker who is forced to wait for many hours without a cigarette is withholding nicotine from his body. This leads to the appearance of symptoms such as irritability, lack of concentration, and frustration. In such cases, it is virtually impossible to remain in a good and calm mood.

This, then, is a real problem, and what is even more disappointing is that smokers are not understood and nor is even a slight degree of tolerance shown towards their situation. When a smoker makes a perfectly innocent mistake and lights a cigarette in a public place where smoking is forbidden, aggressive non-smokers will immediately appear and jump on him as if recoiling in disgust, shame him, and order him to put it out immediately.

This approach is often upsetting and insulting to smokers, as smokers are in fact, like the general public, ordinary people who by chance became smokers in the course of their lives and at this particular stage are inhibited by this addiction. Smokers are no less considerate towards others than non-smokers. In fact, their awareness of their smoking tends to make them sometimes even more sensitive to the feelings of others and to the importance of not disturbing them. However, since non-smokers have no understanding of the situation in which the smoker finds himself and of his needs, they often tend to relate to him as someone who deliberately lights a cigarette in a restricted area and acts in a malicious way in order to intentionally bother those around him.

As is the case in many other instances, there are two sides to every coin and we have to admit that smokers also do not properly understand non-smokers. I sometimes get to read the responses of smokers to internet articles about the laws related to the prevention of smoking in public places and the various reports about the enforcement of these laws and prosecutions related to this issue. In these responses smokers often complain of being hounded by the general public. The most common complaint is 'what do they want from us? We don't want to interfere with the freedom of any non-smoker to live his life, but they must also give us scope and allot places for smoking.'

Generally this complaint is very reasonable, but looking at it from a wider perspective and over time, it has to be understood that we are in the midst of a process which began in a set of circumstances that were very different from the reality of today. For most of the last century, the phenomenon of smoking was so widespread and accepted that there was almost no public place where people didn't smoke. In shops, banks, post offices, airports, planes, theatres and cinemas, government meetings, and almost everywhere else. Non-smokers had no option other than to accept what, from their perspective, was an unfortunate reality.

More seriously, during most of this period there was no public awareness of the harm caused by smoking in general, and to passive smokers in particular. Thus, even though they were in many instances a majority, non-smokers all over the world got used to accepting as standard the unpleasant smell of cigarette smoke and its suffocating effect in closed areas.

The public image of the smoker as tough, brave, and modern, became an integral part of the culture. Anyone who looks at mid 20th century Hollywood movies can see that everyone was smoking, everywhere and all the time.

Today, the world is undergoing a process of sobering up in relation to smoking. This remark is not aimed at the problem of the individual smoker but rather at a social perspective.

At meetings many smokers say to me 'I so hated smoking before I started' and 'until I myself began to smoke I was one of those who got angry with smokers and came down hard on them.' From this it seems that even smokers suffered from smoking when they themselves were non-smokers. And as we all know, at one point in time all of us were non-smokers. Thus, those who have in fact changed their approach are the smokers whose way of thinking has altered along the way, and whose new stance has become a necessity due to their need to smoke.

The approach of non-smokers on the other hand, has remained the same. However, as we have already explained in the chapter dealing with the addiction experience, non-smokers don't really fully understand the smoker's addiction and are therefore not tolerant enough.

Ironically, some of the youngsters who today protest most loudly against smokers, are liable to find themselves offended by that same attitude of intolerance if they themselves one day become smokers.

LIFE'S DAILY ROUTINE

Over time, a self-definition has been formed within us, the implication of which is – 'I am a smoker'. That is to say, I am a person who in various places and situations in my daily life find myself smoking cigarettes.

Each of us has his own patterns and often these patterns differ from person to person. Be that as it may, smokers routinely find themselves with a cigarette in hand in all sorts of places and situations: in the morning with their coffee; talking on the phone; at meetings; during cigarette breaks; while driving; watching TV; sitting at the computer; at work; waiting for a bus or taxi; at the entrance to a shopping mall; in a bar; in smoking areas at airports, outside hospitals, and so on. And this is so not only in the context of certain places, but also in the context of particular situations: a cigarette after a meal; before a meeting; on a trek; after physical exercise; when bored; in situations of pressure and anxiety; while playing card games; when listening to music; while trying to study, and so on. The cigarettes are there, they are with us and by our side. The pack that we make sure we take wherever we go, the lighter or matches, the ashtrays.

This and more; there are a whole range of behaviors that are linked to smoking and unique to smokers. Among them, the skills we acquired holding the cigarette between our fingers and in our mouths; the lighting of a cigarette as one hand holds a lighter while the other hand is held protectively above it to block the wind; lightly tapping the cigarette to let the ash drop; and there are also those who know how to blow smoke rings.

Not long ago, while I was on my way to a meeting, I saw two people coming out of an office building for a cigarette break. They were talking and one of them already held a cigarette in one hand and a lighter in the other as he exited the building; the second person, still preoccupied with their conversation, wasn't yet holding a cigarette but could be seen pulling out a pack and a lighter from his shirt pocket while he continued to talk. A few seconds later, as if there was an agreed signal between them, they stopped talking and lit their cigarettes. The first smoker lit his quickly, inhaled deeply and exhaled the smoke. He turned his head slightly to one side so that the smoke would not go directly into the face of his companion. The second smoker took a cigarette out of the pack, lit it, and deliberately exhaled the smoke of his first drag in an upward direction by slightly bending his head backwards in order to prevent the smoke from reaching his friend's face.

The actions of smokers are mostly automatic; they don't pay attention to their behavior as it is viewed by an observer. There is a range of actions and behavioral patterns we adopt quite naturally in the course of our smoking career. It is interesting, by the way, that smokers too try to avoid the exhaled smoke. On the one hand they inhale the smoke deeply into their lungs, while on the other hand the exhaled smoke, if blown directly at someone – be he a smoker or a non-smoker – is liable to sting that person's eyes and produce a suffocating, unpleasant smell. Smokers are aware of that and refrain from exhaling directly at anyone and instead make sure that the smoke is blown either upwards, downwards, or sideways, by bending their heads or pursing their lips.

All these examples, illustrating situations in daily life are, in effect, pictures of our reality. We see ourselves with cigarettes in a very large number of such pictures, with the result being consolidated over the years making it difficult for us to even imagine a different reality.

This is the tight grip of the addiction to cigarettes which combines with our routine daily feelings of physical craving. The physical craving arouses a sense of discomfort and is followed by an almost automatic thought linking the place and situation in which we find ourselves with a cigarette. With the passage of time, a reality is formed so that in many situations it doesn't seem natural to us to be without a cigarette.

This happens a lot whether or not we need more nicotine. Even if we have only recently finished a cigarette break and suddenly an important telephone call comes in, it is likely that we will light up again. There is also, in situations of stress while watching a game, or in situations of pressure and anxiety, a tendency to smoke one cigarette after another – commonly known as chain smoking. There is no doubt that the reason for lighting another cigarette on such occasions has nothing to do with the level of nicotine in the blood since the previous cigarette was smoked only moments earlier. Except that the associative context – the first thought that comes into our mind – doesn't take that into account. To us it still seems that something is missing and that this something is a cigarette.

This phenomenon is one of the main obstacles that prevents smokers from being set free of cigarettes. Without an understanding of this reality and proper guidance as to how to bring about change, it is almost impossible to quit smoking. Many smokers who try to stop without the preparation and acquisition in advance of the necessary knowledge are simply not at all dealing with the psychological aspect. The result is that the thinking patterns remain in place and are sometimes even reinforced.

In such cases a person goes around all the time with feelings of distress and lack. As he finds himself having to face life's problems, he again visualizes pictures from the past of smoking a cigarette in similar situations and he feels frustrated. This is a sad war of attrition and at the end of the day it leads to a return to smoking. Women who smoke but abstain during pregnancy, or people who are forced to refrain from smoking during a temporary illness, don't usually quit smoking but rather wait with anticipation for the moment when it will be possible for them to go back to it.

This is also the case in relation to many smokers who try to quit without understanding how the addiction works. I call them 'smokers on a break'. By definition these are people who define themselves as smokers, except that for now they are abstaining. Generally, a break, by its very nature, is temporary. We go out for breaks now and then, but breaks are brief periods of time within our lives and not life itself.

The path we take to be set free of smoking depends, to a large extent, on our ability to understand how our mental system works, what activates it, and how it is possible, with relative ease, to influence it in the direction that we want.

CHAPTER 2

The Way Thinking Evolves in Relation to Smoking

When we started to smoke we had to acquire a new skill which was not a simple task for us – learning to smoke. This task requires a significant effort in dealing with the smoke, with the burning sensation in the eyes, and the feeling of suffocation in the throat and lungs. Success in overcoming these difficulties was achieved gradually and by our being persistent.

At the beginning, we don't really know how to inhale the smoke into our lungs. Young smokers inhale it into their mouths and exhale it with almost no fumes entering the lungs. This generally satisfies them for a while because people begin smoking by imitating the more practiced smokers around them. Since the most conspicuous aspect is an inhalation and exhalation of smoke, so far as the beginner is concerned it makes no real difference whether or not the smoke is drawn into the lungs.

If already doing it, then for him it is definitely preferable to inhale the smoke into the mouth and then exhale without drawing it in into the lungs, since inhalation into the lungs involves the feeling of suffocation, a sore throat, and coughing.

From an external perspective, the appearance of smoking can be achieved very well without inhaling all the way into the lungs. Smoke is inhaled, the tip of the cigarette glows, and exhalation reveals thick plumes of smoke exiting the smoker's mouth. When I was a smoker I came across someone who had been smoking for a number of years without inhaling it into his lungs until a more experienced smoker put him right. As much as it saddens me to say this, the experienced smoker was me.

Slowly, and in stages, we learn to inhale small quantities into our lungs. In many cases this happens without the aid of an experienced smoker and is simply the result of the nicotine effect. Whether or not we ourselves inhale the smoke into our lungs, an amount of nicotine inevitably penetrates the lungs and the blood stream. The nicotine's action creates the craving which gradually increases and produces a stronger inclination to inhale a little bit more into the lungs each time we smoke. At one and the same time we get used to coping with the smoke and the sore feeling in the throat while our taste buds and sense of smell adjust to the new state.

Everything we learn that is connected to developing our skills is acquired in a similar way. An instructive example of this can be seen from observing the way in which infants learn to walk. In the first year of life the infant isn't aware of his body's ability and begins to move himself only when he is already a few months old. After that, the activation of the muscles of his hands and legs for the purpose of crawling from place to place is accomplished mostly via natural instincts.

When he progresses to the next phase of standing and walking, he is able, as an observer, to see adults who walk around him quite naturally and these impressions are registered. The attempt to stand up while holding on to an item of furniture – a table, a chair or bed – as well as the act of walking which begins with a few steps and then a stumble, are actions that imitate those older than him without the infant understanding the meaning of what he is doing.

He doesn't take an informed decision to start learning to walk because he understands the advantages embodied in walking as opposed to crawling. Rather, he discovers these possibilities from observation and imitation of those bigger than him. When infants manage to walk, and even to run a bit, their conduct remains unstable and inconstant because they haven't yet actually acquired the skills related to these actions. The ability to walk steadily, and even to run properly, is acquired over time by repeated attempts until complete control over the body is achieved.

CONSCIOUS AND SUBCONSCIOUS THINKING

As we saw in the earlier chapters that dealt with our physical systems, embedded within us as humans is an efficient and sophisticated structure that enables us to operate and function optimally. Something similar also exists in our mental system. We are creatures that learn and develop and, at least theoretically, there is apparently no limit to these human capacities. Our consciousness and thoughts are fashioned in a way that makes such a reality possible.

Together with our conscious activities, the reality we are concerned with at any given moment – such as the fact that you are right now preoccupied with the reading of this book – there is the parallel activity of our subconscious. The subconscious is related, among other things, to the knowledge we acquired about reality at some time in the past. However, this knowledge does not require us to consciously refer to it. At any given time the conduct of our lives when we are awake involves a constant integration between these two levels of consciousness.

For example, in the morning when we are getting ready for a new day, we stand in front of the wardrobe scanning the clothes folded in front of us, and then select a certain shirt and a particular pair of pants. This process of scanning and choosing is a conscious process. It is carried out by us consciously and we are aware of the fact that at this moment we are busy doing something – in this case choosing the clothes we intend to wear. If a member of the household happens to go into the next room without seeing us and asks us what we are doing, we will probably say that we are choosing what to wear or simply that we are getting dressed.

Generally, we can only think consciously of one thing at a time. We sometimes assume that we have the ability to think about a number of different things in parallel, but it isn't really so. What appears to be our ability to simultaneously think about various things is, in fact, a capacity to let our thoughts run at great speed from one issue to another. For example, we are able to play chess with a friend and while doing this to talk on the phone; from time to time we can also glimpse the newspaper headlines, and even think about what we would like to order in the restaurant we are going to go to for dinner. But each time we turn to actually becoming occupied with one of these matters, we will be unable to consciously think about something else. Nonetheless, there is very nearly simultaneity because we are able to shift from one issue to another in a matter of just a few seconds and even less than that.

On the other hand, actions that require non conscious thought, that is to say actions that are accomplished subconsciously, can occur really simultaneously to our conscious thinking. Let's return to the example of getting organized in the morning. After we have picked the clothes and begin to get dressed, we need to move our limbs skillfully. We need to insert one leg into the trousers, then the other leg, put on the shirt by pushing our hands through the sleeves and finally button up. These things seem trivial to us and generally speaking we don't tend to devote any thought to them. And this is precisely the issue – these are actions that belong to our subconscious thinking.

There *is* a thought process involved. The skill of knowing how to dress isn't a natural attribute acquired from nowhere. For the small child, for instance, these actions are complex, but for the adult they require almost no attention.

Given that, we have the ability to continue to operate our conscious thinking in tandem with getting dressed. So it is that while we are still getting dressed we are, at the same time, able to think about the tasks we have to perform during the day ahead and about various other things: taking the children to kindergarten and school; the shopping we have to do; reminding ourselves to pay the electricity and phone bills; to postpone the meeting we had set for lunchtime; to make an appointment at the hairdresser, and so on. All of this while we are getting dressed and even glimpsing in the mirror.

The option of doing things simultaneously is a valuable asset which most of us tend to ignore. Think for a moment about what might happen if we had to acquire the skill of getting dressed from scratch every day. So much time would be wasted for nothing on something we had already learned to do. We would have to occupy our conscious mind each day to learn the very same thing we had already learned to do the day before. Moreover, we wouldn't be able to think consciously about other things while we were getting dressed.

This reality of possessing a skill that does not require any special attention began with all of us as conscious thought. When we were children and learned how to get dressed, we were indeed consciously preoccupied in acquiring this knowledge. The process of getting dressed even seemed to us to be complex given that we were small and our abilities were limited.

This passage from conscious to subconscious thought happens gradually. As we repeat an action we have learned time and again, assuming that the action is identical each time, the level of concentration and conscious attention required from our brain in order to perform the action, decreases. This is how, from an early age, we acquired all the basic skills; standing, walking, running, dressing, brushing our teeth, doing up shoelaces, writing, opening doors, going up and down stairs, eating with a knife and fork or chopsticks, and so on.

At a certain point in our past history all of these represented a challenge for us and very much preoccupied our conscious thinking. But over the years, as these actions were repeated time after time they turned into some sort of second nature for us, and from then on required almost no conscious attention. While we get dressed in the morning, brush our teeth, make coffee, and get organized, we can think about, and be preoccupied with, other issues that require our conscious attention, such as the tasks we need to perform, ideas we have, problems we need to resolve, etc.

SMOKING WHILE DOING OTHER THINGS

The phenomenon of smoking is no exception in this regard. The skills we learned in order to smoke have long since moved from the conscious to the subconscious. The initial process of learning is not particularly long, and coping with the smoke and the smell becomes easier and easier as we continue smoking. The constant repetition of the identical actions turns these actions into a naturally integral part of our lives that requires no attention or conscious thought.

If you observe people smoking, you will notice a wide range of situations in which smokers pay almost no attention to the behavioral actions in relation to their smoking. A smoker really focused on whatever he is doing, can read a newspaper, or work on his computer, and while doing so take a cigarette from the pack, light it, flick the ash into the ashtray, and do it all almost without even glancing at any of these actions. Our conduct with cigarettes becomes automatic as long as our daily procedure of repetition is maintained.

Similarly to the other basic skills which we acquired we have a natural tendency to make use of the ability to perform trivial actions such as smoking while doing other things either actively, or passively, as when, say, reading or watching something. Over time, smoking becomes something that is done 'while' – while preparing and drinking coffee, while talking, while on our way running errands, while working on the computer, while reading a book or newspaper, and also while taking in the view during a walk, or while sitting or lying down and thinking.

This reality is unsurprising; smoking itself, being an action that is repeated so many times, no longer requires our active awareness. We live our lives, busy doing what we have to do, and from time to time feel a certain sense of emptiness and disquiet that we interpret as a need to smoke. Our response to these feelings is to light a cigarette which does, indeed, give us relief for a time, and we try and get on with our tasks without paying any attention to the matter. Only on those occasions when we are forced to go outside for a cigarette break because of some restriction – for example, workplaces where smoking is not permitted – are we a bit more aware of smoking as a separate act.

Yet smoking as such is not our real motive for going out for a cigarette break. Our real motive is to temporarily relieve a feeling of distress. Thus, quite naturally, while we smoke during a cigarette break that has been forced upon us we preoccupy ourselves with other things.

It is essential that we pay attention to this. When smokers feel a pressure to go out for a cigarette break, the break is not for the purpose of having a cigarette as an action in and of itself, but rather a break to get a 'fix', an action aimed at getting a dose of nicotine and calming ourselves down. Because of this, smokers seek to go out for their cigarette breaks with other smokers or, alternatively, take their cell phone with them or something to read that will keep them busy during the cigarette break. For some reason or other when smokers find themselves alone during a cigarette break without a parallel additional activity they feel bored.

BECOMING A SMOKER BY DEFINITION

Long ago, smoking for us became a means rather than an objective. There is an additional aspect of our subconscious mind here. Not only physical skills become part of our subconscious thinking ability. Perceptions also form in our subconscious through repetition. Within the framework of our daily lives we constantly absorb impressions of our surroundings and of ourselves. In line with the reality surrounding us, there develops an adjustment of our conduct and our lifestyle, such as the way we dress, our way of talking, the choice of friends we make, and so on.

For most people, irrespective of what it is they are busy with during the day, the routine of their lives is pretty fixed, so that while multiplying and repeating daily actions a lifestyle develops for each one of us. This is expressed in a certain routine way of dressing, especially among men, the types of food we eat and when we eat, our regular hobbies etc. Things we're used to doing every day and the way in which we do them become part of who we are – of our personality. We absorb impressions – that are in effect pictures of our reality in all sorts of different situations – and link these impressions to the way in which we define our self-image.

The average smoker of twenty cigarettes a day sees himself with a cigarette in hand in all sorts of daily situations. As this pattern of behavior occurs over months and years it also becomes a thinking pattern. The meaning of this is that not only am I actually smoking, I am also a smoker by way of definition – I identify myself as a smoker. This develops into a sort of perceptual stance. It affects the physical craving and is also affected by that craving, but this perception also exists on another level and has a life of its own.

Perceptions that form in our subconscious are created in a quiet process that, with the passage of time, establishes deep roots without us usually noticing it. The absurdity is that it is while we actually acquire the skill of smoking – a process involving our conscious thought – that the beginner's basic assumption is that the addiction won't get him. No beginner wants to become addicted and he evaluates his relation to cigarettes as someone who defines himself as a non-smoker, and who is momentarily trying out a brand new experience.

We start off our smoking career with the determined approach that cigarettes are not part of our way of life, nor do we have any intention of them becoming part of our lives in the future. It's fine for us to amuse ourselves with smoking particularly since we don't see ourselves as smokers in terms of our self-definition.

Within a few months the balance of power changes and the need to smoke is noticeable though we don't yet have a clear understanding of this. After smoking for only a few months the thinking patterns are not yet sufficiently formed, which is an entirely different situation from our present mindset after years of smoking.

The patterns are formed layer by layer and day after day of smoking. With the passage of time, the daily number of cigarettes increases, the cigarettes are integrated into more and more situations in our lives, and the adjustment of our lifestyle to the new reality intensifies.

In the light of this process we become weaker. The irritability and lack of inner serenity lead us to fill the void with more and more nicotine in the course of which a mental process is formed that links the cigarette with our subconscious perceptions.

CHAPTER 3

Formation of Thinking Patterns

We all have a kind of inner voice that conducts some sort of a dialogue with us. Many call it the 'little man' inside. For example, before getting out of the car on our way to a social event, it sometimes occurs to us to take one last quick look in the mirror to ensure our hair is properly styled or that we look OK in the clothes we are wearing. Or as can be seen in another example, a short while after we leave the house for work the following inner dialogue takes place: 'Did I lock the door? Did I turn off the gas or the lights?' We all have a sort of internal thought mechanism that functions as if watching from the sidelines and regularly sends us messages. The same 'observer' also alerts us occasionally to feel out our pockets while walking in the street or anywhere else, and make sure that our pack of cigarettes is there.

This 'observer' does not operate out of awareness, but rather through some kind of an inner voice that is based on experience, the multiplication, and the repetition of our actions. This inner voice is founded on the variety of situations and experiences accumulated in the course of our lives.

Our ability to observe and process the information is incessant, and through repeated observation in different situations in our lives, basic thinking patterns are formed. Meaning that by finding ourselves or seeing others in embarrassing situations – say arriving at a social event disheveled or sloppily dressed – a defense mechanism is created that alerts us to check ourselves before we go into the function. Or, alternatively, since our past experience taught us that forgetting the pack of cigarettes in the car or at home is likely to create unease because of a shortage of cigarettes, subconscious thinking patterns are formed that alert us to occasionally check our pockets to confirm that the cigarette pack is still with us.

Through our subconscious thinking patterns basic assumptions and attitudes are shaped in relation to our being smokers. During the course of our lives as smokers we hear ourselves expressing various set phrases in relation to smoking such as 'I must have a cigarette', when we feel pressed to go for cigarette break, or 'there's nothing like a cigarette after a meal', which we say to ourselves and to our fellow smokers as we go out of the restaurant for a smoke.

As such phrases are repeated over and over again dozens and hundreds of times, an associative connection begins to be formed – a conditioning – between certain actions in our lives and the smoking of a cigarette.

And it's not just expressions that are relevant in this matter but also various situations in our lives, examples of which we have already mentioned like a cigarette with a cup of coffee, on the beach when looking at some view, in the car in a traffic jam, or in the course of a regular ride, after physical exercise, and so on. In all such situations a subconscious thought is formed that says 'you are a smoker, in these situations you need a cigarette.'

RETROSPECTIVE THINKING PATTERNS

In the 'Smokefree way' meetings we ask the participants to indicate the benefits they get from smoking. In the main, the thinking patterns that we are all familiar with are repeated – smoking is enjoyable, it relieves stress, suppresses appetite, helps in concentration, relaxes, passes the time, increases self-confidence, and assists digestion. We list all these elements on the white board since every one of them deserves to be explored individually.

But before that, we ask the participants a general question: Did you form these attitudes consciously? In other words, did you from the outset think that cigarettes would help you with all these things and as a result became smokers? Or are all these perceptions retrospective, some sort of explanation we attach to an existing situation?

The unambiguous reply that emerges from what participants say is that these are retrospective perceptions and assumptions. No starting smoker logically analyses the pros and cons involved in smoking and then makes a conscious decision to join the addicts group.

As humans, we have a natural tendency to try and avoid becoming addicted. As a result of us being free creatures of independent thought it is difficult for us to accept authority and constraint; we don't like being lead and out of control. People addicted to cigarettes, or to anything else for that matter, don't consciously choose addiction.

However, when we find ourselves in a given situation in which we have to continue to smoke out of an urge that is aroused within us a number of times a day, we begin to link the situations in which we smoke to a perception of some sort. In other words, we need to create an explanation of some kind for what we are doing.

Since the reality of our being smokers is an established fact, and the physical urge is not perceived by us as the primary reason for smoking, we don't say 'I have to go for a cigarette break because there is a lack of nicotine in my body, and it is this shortage that is causing me to be irritable and restless.' Instead we simply say 'I need to go out for a cigarette to calm down.'

What we see here is an amazing process involving the formation of a subconscious standpoint by what is usually termed 'cognitive bias', which is to say a misconception that is based on the way we interpret the reality.

Our tendency is to always focus on the cigarette which we have just lit because that is what really eases our condition. We don't pay attention to the fact that it is this cigarette that is responsible for maintaining our need for nicotine, and that it is this need itself that is responsible for creating the sense of irritability and restlessness within us. In other words, the fact that we are smokers and that we smoked the previous cigarette are, from the beginning, the reasons for our excessive irritability. These are the primary reasons why we have to concern ourselves in any way with easing our condition and calming down.

If we were entirely smokefree, there would be no need for us to calm down with the help of a cigarette because a situation in which we needed to calm down would not have been created. Because of our failure to recognize this fact we tend to think that it is the cigarette itself that calms us down, and that the stress we are coping with is part and parcel of the stressful situations that stem from the general lifestyle.

This is perhaps one of the most central issues in the phenomenon of the addiction to cigarettes which it is important for us to understand. We have to acknowledge the fact that the addiction to cigarettes resembles a vicious circle in which every cigarette creates the need for the next one.

In the framework of this lifestyle depicted earlier in the lower of the two drawings – as an allegory for a more inferior lifestyle than nature already provides us with – we have to cope daily with a range of problems that are created by smoking and which are correspondingly temporarily eased by smoking.

Another significant factor in this context is that cigarettes do not ease the problems relating to the real issues in our lives that are not connected to smoking. On the contrary, the fact that we are smokers is, rather, an additional burden for us and weakens us. The reality of our being smokers is expressed in feelings of unease at various levels and a permanent lack of inner calm, and this is the reason why in the course of a day we routinely experience ups and downs.

Unfortunately we don't tend to compare our feelings to those of non-smokers and as a result we fail to notice that this situation of ours is unnatural. It seems to us that this is what life is like for all adults. Moreover, these feelings are not generally subjected to our awareness and such things happen in the background of our lives. All the while that we have a feeling of imbalance we try to hurry and light another cigarette, so that the additional dose of nicotine will help us to push away the unease for a while longer.

It remains for us now to relate to the main mindsets that are identified by smokers as benefits from smoking, and to examine them on the basis of the features that form and construct them. Each such stance separately reflects a foothold of the addiction to smoking that was unintentionally formed over time.

By this examination and process of scrutiny, we are able to observe from a different viewpoint than we are used to, and allow ourselves to get new insights similarly to the way we have done throughout the reading so far.

The reading and acknowledgment of things continue to bring a significant change in the way we understand and experience our addiction to cigarettes even though this is not yet expressed in a practical way. Not to worry. In the coming chapters we complete the entire process of understanding the addiction in all its aspects, and we will then safely go about changing course towards setting free from the addiction once and for all.

CHAPTER 4

Stressful Situations and Chain Smoking

The fact is that every smoker experiences two types of stress in his life without usually distinguishing between them. One type of stress is routine and related to smoking in accordance with the amount of nicotine consumed by the body. This is a relatively mild level of stress that we have grown used to living with, without paying too much attention to it. Sometimes it is more sensed and sometimes less, depending on our daily intake of nicotine. This mild form of stress that is entirely due to our smoking is also regularly eased by smoking another cigarette. It is in no way connected to our life situation at any given moment – it is a stress that stems only from smoking.

At the same time for smokers and non-smokers alike, there are situations of stress that are related to problems in life with which we all have to deal: health problems of ours or those close to us; economic difficulties; pressures at work; stresses in our personal relations; pressure in studying and before exams; while watching sporting events; when playing cards – especially if that involves a monetary gamble.

In these and all other situations of stress related to external events, coping with and overcoming the state of tension is directly linked to the event itself. In such external situations of stress, smoking cigarettes does not ease the condition nor have a calming effect despite our tendency to think that it does, in fact, help. This can be verified by looking closely at our behavioral patterns in these situations.

When we feel stressed by an external event our tendency is to smoke more cigarettes than usual – what smokers call chain smoking. A good example of this is a smoker waiting tensely in the smoking area outside a hospital department while someone close to him is undergoing a dangerous operation or some other major form of treatment. The smoker, like other relatives waiting with him, is worried and stressed. He, like everyone else, is hoping to hear positive news from the medical team the moment the operation is finished or the treatment has ended. We can add another example of stress due to an external event of a smoker waiting outside the maternity ward while his wife is giving birth. The stressed smoker is waiting with eager anticipation for the doctor or the midwife to come and tell him that the baby has been born and that everything is OK.

In cases of this kind, as in situations of stress resulting from other external events, many smokers tend to chain smoke – smoking more and more cigarettes one after the other.

If the cigarettes really reduced the stress we would supposedly be seeing that people who smoke do indeed relax as a result of smoking, and manage to pass the tense waiting period in a really calm way compared to their non-smoking friends. Moreover, if the cigarettes really eased the stress of an external event, then only a few cigarettes would be required to create a feeling of relief for a while. Chain smoking actually points to the fact that smoking cigarettes does not lead to a relief from stress, and anyone observing from the sidelines would undoubtedly describe the smoker as looking tenser than those around him.

The reality of decreasing stress through smoking applies only to the mild daily stress we experience that is related to the amount of nicotine in the body. A smoker who finds himself in a state of stress due to an external event and begins to chain smoke, significantly increases the level of nicotine in his body after the first or second cigarette. That eliminates the stress he experiences linked to his smoking. What he is then left with is the stress that is directly linked to the external event. That stress will be eased by the event itself coming to an end – for example news from the medical team that everything is OK and that the operation or treatment is in its final stages. Given that the cigarettes don't contribute to the easing of the stress of an external event, they won't be of any help here. It is the external event itself that is responsible for raising the level of stress, so that only progress or an end to the event will bring about a reduction in the level of stress.

MENTAL CONDITIONING AND THE SOURCE OF STRESS

The above intensifies the question of why, after all, there is a tendency to smoke a great deal more than usual in externally stressful situations. The answer to this question uncovers the substantive link between smoking and our subconscious thinking patterns.

In our daily routine we experience, day after day, the mild stress which is related to smoking itself and the level of nicotine in our bodies. This mild and permanent form of stress emerges within the average smoker about fifteen to twenty times a day. Accordingly, the smoker relieves this stress by lighting an equivalent number of cigarettes. As this process continues over a period of months and years, a mental conditioning develops. This conditioning is an expression of our subconscious thinking linking the general term 'stress' to the smoking of a cigarette.

As smokers, we usually fail to observe what causes this constant stress, though it is very clear to us what calms it down for a while. What calms this daily stress is the next cigarette. Each time, the cigarette we light slightly eases the feeling of stress that returns and emerges within us over and over again during the day. What is etched in our minds is the linkage between the two concepts, 'stress' and 'having a cigarette'.

When we are dealing with the stress of an external event, the mental conditioning is not able to take the source of the stress into account. This is not a conscious analytical thought such as the one we are performing at this moment. The conditioning is a kind of automatic response and comes to our aid in accordance with the system embedded within us – that everything we are used to repeating over and over again, passes over time into our subconscious thinking patterns.

Thus for the smoker, all stress, no matter what its source, immediately creates a mental urge for a cigarette. Since no distinction is made between different sorts of stress, smoking a cigarette will simply not ease any of the stresses connected with an external source. Without our noticing, what happens is that the cigarette we smoked didn't actually help us and we are left with the same level of tension. As a result, the conditioning to have another cigarette emerges and again, because the stress is external, there is no relief. So we have another one and then another.

There is a kind of trap here. On the one hand our conditioning to have another cigarette as a response to a stressful situation does not cease until there is a relief from that stress, while on the other hand such relief will not come from cigarettes but only from the ending of the event itself. Thus we smoke one after the other until we find ourselves chain smoking.

It is important to indicate that these processes are taking place in the background of our lives. Our tendency is to always accept our feelings and responses as self-evident. We don't stop for a moment and ask what lies behind the phenomenon of chain smoking in a situation of increased stress, or why this compulsive smoking doesn't really calm us. As a result, our mental conditioning becomes increasingly entrenched until the whole phenomenon of chain smoking itself becomes a necessity. It seems to us that this is our only way of coping with these situations.

This is the way things really are in relation to what smokers think of as the relief of stress by smoking. This misconception occurs because time and again we find ourselves holding a cigarette without realizing that our behavioral pattern is an outcome of compulsive conditioning rather than of conscious thinking.

The false perception that cigarettes relieve stress is an interpretation or explanation that we provide to ourselves about a behavioral phenomenon of ours. In fact, this explanation is also not given in a conscious way. A smoker who finds himself in a situation in which he begins to chain smoke doesn't really expect the cigarettes to calm him down.

The smoker is simply compelled to smoke another one and then yet another because he feels an irritation which he interprets as 'I need another cigarette'. We don't even deceive ourselves into thinking that we will really be less stressed as result of this continuous smoking. Only if a non-smoker should come by and ask 'why are you smoking so much?' will our answer be 'because I have to relieve the stress.' Only then will we be required to give this explanation. And this, to put it bluntly, is not an explanation but an excuse. 'Why am I smoking? Because I have to.' And the emphasis is on the 'have to' and not on the relief of stress.

BETWEEN UNDERSTANDING AND ACTING

As smokers we are generally not aware of our true state. And even if we were, it would be very difficult for us to say, for example, 'I am smoking now because I feel a strong internal urge that won't let go. This urge causes me to smoke another cigarette and then another even though that doesn't really help me and doesn't reduce the stress.' It would be very difficult for us to say such things because the human thinking mechanism cannot come to terms with a contradiction between our understanding, on the one hand, and our actions on the other.

Whenever we do something there has to be a compatibility between what we do and our understanding that we are acting correctly. When we identify an error in what we are doing our natural inclination is to change the action according to our renewed understanding.

Say we are on a trip abroad in a hired car. Looking at maps and signposts, it becomes clear that we are travelling in the wrong direction. What we then do is to immediately turn around and start to travel in a different direction.

While we retain a doubt as to the right direction, we can continue on the same route since there remains a possibility that we are, in fact, on the right road. But the minute we clearly understand that we are going in the wrong direction, we cannot accept this information and at the same time continue along the same route – a route that is, in any case, no longer of interest to us. The interest we had in the route we were taking thus far was based on the assumption that we had opted for a way that would bring us closer to where we want to be. The moment we realize that the way we are going is actually distancing us from our desired destination we lose interest in that pathway.

It is upon this important foundation that the 'Smokefree way' program is based. The program aims to shed light on the real course of our lives as smokers and to place the true direction of this lifestyle on our agenda. It is a lifestyle we didn't consciously choose to follow and which, through a gradual and sophisticated process, has distorted the way in which we interpret the reality of our daily lives. The moment we realize that the format of our daily lives in fact distances us from precisely those things which we thought cigarettes are giving us, we begin to lose interest in our present pathway and become interested in changing direction.

It is not only that cigarettes do not ease the stress in various situations that occur in our lives; cigarettes actually make the problem worse and increase our difficulty in dealing with it. The reality of our being smokers disrupts the natural balance of our brain's functioning. The natural capabilities we possess to deal with situations of pressure and stress are weakened in the same way as are our taste buds and sense of smell. The fact that as smokers we are more stressed in our daily lives makes us more vulnerable and weaker in all sorts of stressful situations that result from external events.

Differences between people can be observed in their varying abilities to cope with the challenges posed by life, and by the differing levels of mental strength and stability displayed by each and every one of us. As smokers, we pay no attention to the extent to which we have been weakened in this context. This can be noticed whenever our supplies of cigarettes are coming to an end and our stress levels rise. Even when it is late at night and we know that nothing terrible will happen to us if we don't smoke for a few hours, this doesn't prevent the feeling of stress from compelling us to roam frantically through the city's streets in search of an open shop or a cigarette machine. Merely looking at the pack in which just a few last cigarettes are left is enough to raise our levels of stress, as was mentioned in earlier chapters.

When we return to being free of the addiction to smoking, our body systems will naturally become once more available to supply us with mental balance and strength in precisely the way that our human structure is intended to work when it is at its best.

As a rule, and without referring to exceptional cases, we don't need external aids in order to cope with stressful situations. Mental strength and stability are internal attributes that we must nurture. All we have to do is avoid the weakening and instability that cigarettes create.

CHAPTER 5

Smoking and Concentration

Similarly to the way our misconceptions with regard to stress relief evolve, so all our viewpoints and perceptions about smoking are formed. Interpreting the reality of various life situations in line with the feeling of relief we get from cigarettes covers up the simple truth that this relief is sought only by smokers, and that it is the fact of our being smokers which creates the difficulty for which we are seeking a relief.

This is also the way in which our perception that smoking helps us to concentrate works. As with the other things, this viewpoint also stems from the difficulty we sometimes have concentrating without a cigarette in our hand. We identify a problem – the difficulty in concentrating, and then perceive an assistant in the cigarette we are smoking. We don't verify for ourselves what it is that is actually disturbing our concentration. All we know is that whenever we find it difficult to focus we light a cigarette and that seems to make it easier for us.

Concentration, no matter on what, whether it be study, watching something or even reading this text, requires the right conditions. The main trait of concentration is the ability to center our attention on one thing while avoiding any distractions from elsewhere. When we focus on a certain object in space, for example, if we are holding a match or a lighter and focus our sight on them, the item we are looking at can be clearly seen by us, whereas everything else in the vicinity becomes blurred.

Concentration, exactly like focusing your sight, requires you to center on one thing so that everything else becomes part of the background. All the cigarettes in the world won't help us to concentrate if, while trying to focus, we are distracted by the phone ringing, the door being slammed, a noisy plane flying above us, or any similar diversion. Except that generally, when we need to concentrate we try to relocate to a place where there are no such external distractions, allowing ourselves to sit peacefully and quietly and concentrate.

But then, while there are no external disturbances, another form of disturbance suddenly appears – a kind of inner restlessness. We don't really pay attention to what causes it but only know that a cigarette will make this disturbance vanish. From this we form the far reaching conclusion that smoking aids concentration.

Though we said that we were trying to relocate ourselves in surroundings free of disturbances, we need to understand that together with ourselves we imported an additional source of disturbance into these surroundings – our perpetual lack of nicotine.

The main conclusion to be deduced from this is that cigarettes are first of all a factor that disrupts our concentration because our being smokers forces us to be in a state of constant imbalance and perpetual restlessness.

Though the lighting of another cigarette temporarily does reduce this inner sense of unease, it does not alter the fact that this state is a direct outcome of our being smokers. Cigarettes can only help us to concentrate when the problem is related to a lack of nicotine.

Since this is the way things are, cigarettes cannot be regarded as an aid to concentration. If cigarettes were really such an aid, then everyone, including those who don't smoke would be able to enjoy this "valuable" remedy.

Cigarettes don't aid concentration, on the contrary, cigarettes disturb concentration, and from time to time appear to slightly ease a phenomenon for whose existence they are themselves responsible. Moreover, if we have to concentrate in places where smoking is not permitted, like exams or meetings, our constant thoughts about the 'next cigarette' further undermine our ability to concentrate.

CHAPTER 6

Smoking and self-Confidence

This close scrutiny of our perceptions in relation to smoking is of great importance. In order to release ourselves from cigarettes and become truly smokefree we must look closely and inspect what we believe to be the benefits we obtain from cigarettes.

Another perception that we need to examine is the notion that cigarettes help with our self-confidence. Though many smokers don't think about it in this way, the fact is that our self-confidence is very closely associated with the idea of self-image – that initial reason that drove almost all youngsters to begin smoking. I know that many smokers say to themselves 'yes, I know that, it was really relevant in an earlier period, but today I don't feel that I actually need cigarettes either for my self-image or my self-confidence.' Even if many of you don't feel it, that doesn't mean that cigarettes don't have a significant influence on your self-confidence.

Let's check this in the following way. You are invited to an event, say a wedding. You drive to the event and park your car in the guest parking lot of the reception hall. You get out of the car and go through the regular 'last minute' check list: hair combed? Yes; appropriately dressed? Yes; got the wedding present? Yes; lighter? Yes; cigarettes?... Oh... where are the cigarettes? We begin a search; trouser pockets, shirt pockets, jacket pockets; cigarettes, eh... yes found them, there's a pack, great. Oh... just a minute, how many are there? Wow, the pack is empty! Perhaps the following thought goes through your mind 'oh yes, I thought about this on the way; I was preoccupied with thoughts while driving and noticed that I only had one cigarette left but said to myself OK, so what? I'll smoke the last one now and when I get closer to the reception hall I'll look for somewhere to buy another pack.'

So far so good. But now what? We go into the hall and begin to review our options. Is there a cigarette machine in the hall? Is there a store open in the area that is within walking distance? How many smokers that we know will be at this event? Our main attention is now focused on the shortage of cigarettes.

It's not that we necessarily need a cigarette right now – it may well be that we have just recently finished smoking the last one – rather our behavior is driven by the importance we attach to having a supply of cigarettes at hand. More accurately, we can say that it's not just important for us to have a cigarette in our hand, but that this is based on the fact that when we don't have a cigarette within reach we actually lose our self-confidence.

At social events, even when we have a sufficient supply of cigarettes, many of us will find themselves going into the hall, of course wishing the celebrants all the best, mingling a bit with the other guests, and then quickly making their way to the smoking area. This will happen even if this area is outside the hall itself where it's pouring with rain, a cold wind is blowing or, alternatively, it's as hot and dry as the desert.

As smokers we have got used to feeling comfortable in social situations only after we have paid a visit to the smoking area. This conduct raises a number of questions that require an answer. Why is it so? Why can't we say to ourselves 'OK, so there aren't any cigarettes, so this evening we won't be smoking and we'll still enjoy the event'? What is it that prevents us from behaving similarly to non-smokers who are able to calmly enter the hall, mingle comfortably with the other people there, sit down at a table and simply enjoy the event without being plagued by the urge to hurry off to an area of dense smoke, or feel compelled to go out of a hall which they entered only a few minutes earlier?

A NATURALLY CONFIDENT FEELING

Over a period of time as smokers we lose our natural self-confidence. The concept of the term 'self-confidence' derives its meaning from the confidence I have in myself, in who I am in the most natural and basic state. When we feel uncomfortable and agitated at a social event and only a cigarette relieves us, it is important that we understand that this situation is a direct result of a deterioration in our natural self-confidence. It stems solely from the reality of our being smokers.

We have already shown in earlier chapters the way in which the deterioration in self-confidence weakens smokers to the extent that they are unable to have a conversation or an argument without a lit cigarette in their hand. Here too, just as in the case of the other thinking patterns, we perceive a reality literally the very opposite to the way things really are. We attribute to the cigarette in our hand a trait that supports our self-confidence when, in fact, we're using the cigarette as a cover for our lack of self-confidence.

In a social context the common image of a smoker is of someone who has something to do while he is smoking. At a social gathering a cigarette enables us to look as if we are busy – lighting up, smoking, settling down in a corner of the room, or looking for the smoking area. All these little preoccupations may signal to those around us that we are not in any way embarrassed.

We have grown used to this conditioning – meaning that in the context of social situations we have conditioned ourselves to interpret our state in a certain way. Hence, when in such circumstances we suddenly find ourselves without cigarettes, or in a place where smoking is prohibited, it becomes very difficult for us to cope with the feeling that we will be seen as being bored or as someone who has nothing to do and also, perhaps, like somebody no one wants to talk to.

Holding a cigarette, on the other hand, creates the illusion for us that we are in possession of some sort of safeguard. This kind of thinking stems solely from the fact that as smokers we have, over the years, lost our natural sense of confidence. In the natural state of the non-smoker there are no such feelings of distress, nor does the non-smoker feel the need to demonstrate confidence to the outside world. Our natural state as non-smokers enables us to feel quite comfortable in all sorts of encounters because we don't have a feeling of anything being missing.

The fact that in social situations we get a sense of relief from cigarettes is a sign that without them something is lacking – a lack that the cigarettes are supposed make up for. And if there is such a lack of confidence it is not due to our personality but rather is based on our being smokers.

In this case as well if, at a social event, we were to give a cigarette to a non-smoker, it would surely not enhance his feelings of self-confidence. On the contrary, it would seem to him strange and ridiculous. And so it would also seem to ex-smokers.

After returning to a natural and normal state without a dependence on cigarettes, we feel great while in the company of others and also in situations which, in the past, were perceived by us as being very much linked to cigarettes.

CHAPTER 7

Passing the Time Smoking

We have got used to living in an upside-down world. In all sorts of situations in our lives the need to smoke arises, and each time we teach ourselves once more to think that we are fine only when we have a cigarette. The truth is that we are supposed to be absolutely fine in every circumstance and at all times by being exactly as we are – without a cigarette. It is amazing how, through the addiction, we have reached such a point in life when it doesn't seem to us at all natural to be without a cigarette. Very good examples of this are situations in which we are idle, stuck in a traffic jam, or waiting in a line for the doctor or a bus.

As a matter of routine, the reality of our being smokers causes us to be less laid back and more ill at ease. Therefore, when we have to wait for something we are not particularly patient, and our impatience increases significantly if the wait also entails not smoking.

Similarly to the way in which the addiction creates a lack of self-confidence within us, having to wait and boredom cause us to hurry up and reach for a cigarette. This happens because when at a social event or idly waiting the thought that immediately arises is 'Well... what do I do now?'

When we are restless and lack internal balance we tend to behave a little bit like kids. It is difficult for us to defer gratification and hard for us to accept that now, while waiting, there is nothing specific for us to do and that is just fine. Additionally, when our mind is not focused on anything in particular, we quite naturally become more aware of the physical feelings that result from our lack of nicotine.

We have accustomed ourselves to quickly light a cigarette in order to reduce such feelings of shortage. The multiplication and repetition of this action conditions us to think that cigarettes help us to pass the time when we have nothing specific to do. At the 'Smokefree way' meetings participants quite often even claim that while waiting for a bus, for example, they feel that it is strange and unnatural for them to just stand there and wait without doing anything. A participant once said 'if I'm waiting for a bus without cigarette I feel like an idiot who's just standing there doing nothing.' Is it really so? Do cigarettes really help us pass the time of day?

If we observe smokers while they wait, we'll see that cigarettes don't in fact keep them busy. A smoker who finds himself in a boring situation and is prompted to light a cigarette, does so very quickly, almost automatically, and cannot be said to be 'busy' smoking. He returns to exactly the same state of boredom he was in seconds earlier before lighting the cigarette.

However, the inner voice that prompted us to light the cigarette – that voice that represents the subconscious thinking – does indeed get a response that for the time being satisfies it; from its point of view we are now doing something. But in practice and consciously, we don't actually feel that time is passing by more quickly. We smoke and continue to feel bored. We certainly don't look at the cigarette with a broad smile and say, 'what a pleasure, how time flies when I'm smoking.'

The practical result of smoking while waiting is to relieve the shortage of nicotine, and respond to our subconscious conditioning that we are seemingly 'doing something now' so to speak. Time doesn't pass more quickly and the response to the subconscious thinking pattern is effective only while we are actually smoking. Our subconscious relates to what is happening in the present. Quite quickly after we finish the cigarette, the inner voice will return and again echo the same mantra 'well, what now? Have another cigarette.'

Many people get so used to their state as smokers that they no longer notice that quite a lot of their basic assumptions in relation to this state reflect unnatural human behavior. Actions that, as a result of the addiction, have become daily events are interpreted by smokers in exactly the opposite way – as something natural and self-evident.

In our meetings we ask how a smoker waiting for a bus or a train looks to a non-smoker; does he appear to be busy? Does it look as if for him 'time flies'? Does he appear to be relaxed and calm on account of the cigarette he is now smoking? Certainly not. Observing the scene objectively from the sidelines, it looks as if the smoker is standing and waiting like everybody else, the only difference being that as well as waiting he also every now and then inhales and exhales smoke. He doesn't look busy nor does he look more relaxed than the others. To the onlooker he appears to be quite foolish precisely because he is smoking.

I once asked a smoker who claimed that he felt like a fool if he wasn't smoking while waiting, whether non-smokers sitting or standing near him also looked to him like fools because they were not lighting up together with him? His answer was 'no', it was only in relation to himself that he felt that way. It was clear to him that this perception stemmed solely from him being a smoker and was relevant only to someone who smoked.

Whether it is while we are in a traffic jam, or are being kept waiting in some other way, the need to smoke arises because of a combination of two things: The feeling of a physical lack together with a tendency we have developed over the years to quickly light a cigarette and create for ourselves the illusion of being busy.

When you'll be set free from the burden of smoking real soon, all the reasons for smoking – physical and mental – will spontaneously disappear, and you'll be left with a gentle and pleasant feeling. Our inner voice will alter its message so that every time we find ourselves waiting with nothing to do, it will remind us that this is absolutely fine and of how great it is to be able to breathe normally and feel relaxed. As ex-smokers you are about to even gain an advantage over non-smokers because, compared to someone who never smoked, the feeling of freedom you will have is much greater. In many situations in which you were used to smoke, your lack of interest in cigarettes will lead to feelings of elation, freedom and good cheer.

CHAPTER 8

Smoking, Enjoyment & Relaxation

Up till now we have gone over a number of assumptions and perceptions that have become embedded within us over the years, and have seen that in certain things there is a common denominator to them all. It's always about perceptions that have been formed retrospectively, never at the beginning. That is to say, no smoker assumes in advance when he chooses to smoke his very first cigarettes that they will help him to concentrate, to pass the time of day, to reduce stress, or turn him into a person brimming with self-confidence. All these perceptions are formed retrospectively at a point at which we found ourselves needing cigarettes to make up for a lack in these areas – deficiencies that in fact result from smoking.

We have seen how, through multiplication and repetition, associative links are formed between our subconscious and various situations in our lives such as when waiting, at social events, in stressful situations, and in situations that require us to concentrate. In all of these circumstances our inner voice is aroused and restates the mantra – 'You need to smoke'. The voice repeats this mantra because we have so often lit a cigarette in all of these situations so that our brain has learned that this action can be consigned to the background of our lives whereupon, because it repeats itself all the time, it becomes just another of those automatic activities that we perform.

Because the action of smoking is repeated so frequently in routine situations, the need for awareness and alertness when performing this act decreases gradually, and smoking becomes a kind of second nature for us – so much so that over time we barely need to pay attention to it any longer. This duplicates the way in which our brain does not make us think consciously about our walking, opening a door, scratching an itch, brushing our teeth, and so on. So too it doesn't require us to think consciously about our smoking. Consequently, misconceptions that smoking is really 'needed' in all sorts of set situations become entrenched within us.

We have also seen that in all these cases smoking doesn't solve anything other than easing the distress we feel, which itself is a result of our being smokers. Therefore, every time we finish a cigarette we still remain stressed, bored, insecure and unfocused. So long as the reasons for these states are external, the amount we smoke – however much that may be – won't help us, and those feelings will remain in place. And the most frustrating thing of all is that because we don't consciously relate to these issues, the fixed thinking pattern simply repeats itself. It is as if it was saying 'you just smoked now? It didn't help you? You are still stressed, bored, feeling socially unconfident? Have another cigarette.'

In practice, a thinking pattern – that is to say a subconscious thought – doesn't ask a question and then answer it. It doesn't work that way. A thinking pattern is merely triggered and responds automatically. It identifies a problem and offers a solution. Every time a situation in which we have been conditioned to have a cigarette arises, our subconscious produces the response – 'have another cigarette'.

It takes no other information into account. The fact that we have just now finished the previous cigarette or that we are already chain smoking and it doesn't help, makes no difference to it. The subconscious has no sense of time nor does it analyze data; that is why we call it the subconscious, meaning, beneath consciousness, or a thinking pattern, which is a constantly recurring or sequential replication of the same perception. The subconscious thought has only one role to play – to give an automatic response in various kinds of circumstances when the point at issue is an action that always repeats itself in such situations.

All this happens due to the fact that we don't consciously pay attention and observe matters. For instance, when we are in any kind of stressful situation, as described in the example of waiting for someone close to us to be treated in hospital, or while watching tense sporting events and in other situations of tension, our conscious thoughts are focused on the event itself. The smoking occurs in the background and we are not free to deal with it or think about it.

Even if for a moment we are reminded of the number of cigarettes we are smoking, for example when some of our friends comment that we are smoking too much, our conscious thinking prefers to affirm the conditioning of our subconscious – to have another cigarette, even when we are already chain smoking. We say 'yes I know, I really am smoking too much, but right now I have to.' From our point of view this isn't the right time to think things over and deal with the problem. Thus we confirm to ourselves the dependence on smoking and strengthen even more the false belief that cigarettes help us.

A UNIQUE PRESUMPTION

The perceptions of enjoyment and relaxation also don't differ from the other perceptions. Relaxation here is not intended to mean a relief of stress but rather it is to be seen in the context of pleasure and enjoyment. Of all the assumptions that smokers hold on to, it seems that our perception that there are cigarettes that we particularly enjoy is the most strongly held of all.

In our meetings, smokers who are reviewing with us the perceptions and beliefs as described in this part one by one, wholeheartedly accept the analysis of reality we apply and the clarifications we have given. Many of them openly admit that it has become clear to them beyond a doubt that the beliefs that formed within them are indeed false and distort the true reality. However, when we come to examine the perceptions of enjoyment and relaxation, the basic presumption is that this aspect is different. So far as almost every smoker is concerned there are situations in which smoking is a pure pleasure.

And indeed, there are plenty of examples to demonstrate this. The most widely known is that of the beach. A description that is repeated by many smokers is of the great pleasure they get smoking cigarettes while sitting on the beach. We've all had the glorious experience of looking out at the beauty and infinite expanse of the sea at sunset or at any other time, with a pleasant breeze caressing our face and the gentle sound of small waves lapping the shoreline as we perhaps sip a beer or a glass of wine. Ahh… for a smoker there is nothing like having a cigarette in these wonderful surroundings.

So it also is with trips to holiday sites as we reach areas of lush vegetation or a high cliff from which we get breathtaking vistas spread out below us. Even if we are on a family holiday with our children and the way to the log cabin has been noisy and jumpy, there is the end of the day to look forward to. By then the children will have gone to sleep or are out on a trek under the supervision of an adult, while we meet up with friends. Everything has calmed down and this is the moment to stretch out on a deck chair or hammock, lean back, sit comfortably and listen to the silence of the surroundings. Nature, the spectacular view, the serenity, like being on top of the world. And here too the cigarette is perceived by us as being the ultimate enhancer of pleasure. Simply fits right in there.

A participant in the cessation program once told me about a trip to France that he went on with friends. As the group went up the Eiffel Tower in the evening, the city's lights twinkled below – a fantastic view from up on high. He then felt he had to have a cigarette. It simply enhances the experience.

This is also true for the cigarette we smoke after various kinds of physical exercise. At times, the cigarette gives us the feeling that in smoking it we are sort of completing the exercise, a clear sign that we have reached the stage of relaxation and rest. Time to have what is known as the cigarette after.

So it seems that when we refer to the enjoyment we get from smoking, we are not talking about situations in which the cigarette is important in dealing better with a difficulty or solving a problem. Rather in this case the approach is that the cigarette does indeed give us some sort of a supplement as if the experience was being intensified by it.

We have to clarify for ourselves whether this perception can withstand a reality check. The meaning of suggesting that cigarettes provide us with this kind of addition and enhancement has to be that it is also possible to enjoy oneself and feel good without it, but that with it, the experience is intensified.

Let's look at the following situation: We are two good friends on our way together to spend a pleasant evening on the beach. I'm the non-smoker, you're the smoker. We reach the seafront and park the car in a parking lot not far from the beach itself. We get out of the car and walk to the beach. With us we have a beach mat, food and drinks and a sound system so that we can play some ambient music in the background. We get to the beach, spread out the mat, and set ourselves up facing the calm sea. This is what we had planned for the evening – having fun and relaxing, and this, for you, is exactly the right time to light a cigarette. You look for the pack and... it's not there. You forgot it in the car. You say to me 'Tamir, wait here, I'll be right back, I have to fetch the cigarettes from the car.

The question is: Why is it so? Why do you have to go back to the car to fetch the cigarettes? If, in this case, all we are talking about is an enhancement of pleasure, it means that we should be able to enjoy anyway, even if on this occasion having a smoke turns out not to be possible. And to someone who says that we have already become used to enhancing the experience by smoking cigarettes, it has to be said that if this is so, then perhaps on this occasion we won't get this extra pleasure but that this shouldn't in any way prevent us from enjoying the evening.

The common behavior of smokers in such situations is expressed by irritability. For a smoker it is very difficult to come to terms with the fact that there are cigarettes within his reach but that he is being prevented from smoking because to do so requires him to make the effort of going all the way to the car and back. It will be very hard for him to ignore this whole thing and enjoy our pleasant evening together even without smoking. From his behavior it will undoubtedly become evident that in the absence of the ability to smoke we are not talking about a lesser level of enjoyment, but rather that without smoking there can be no enjoyment at all. In the vast majority of such situations, particularly if there is no other reason preventing us from returning to the vehicle, practically every smoker will hurry back to the parking lot to fetch the pack.

Another example I can tell you about is of a group of friends who met up to spend a pleasant evening together in the home of one of them, in a small remote village. When at the very beginning of the evening they became aware that they had only very few cigarettes left, the immediate response was to focus on the task of getting additional supplies as quickly as possible. The responsibility for this was given to another friend who was still on his way, warning him that their evening together was likely to come to a rapid halt if the supply of cigarettes wasn't replenished. This is not behavior that can be associated with pleasure. This is not the way those who need cigarettes merely to have more fun with friends would act.

Let's go back for a moment to the previous example and continue with it. Let's say that you went back to the car park, opened the car and discovered the pack but that there was only one cigarette left. Would your reaction be one of real happiness that you have a cigarette which you will be able to enjoy and enhance the experience of the evening? Or would you be gripped by a feeling of disappointment – 'dammit, only one left.' The answer is clear. The feeling will be one of frustration. We have reached a point in our lives when it seems to us that without a cigarette we simply cannot enjoy ourselves. The physical need is there all the time and it is obvious to us that one cigarette won't be enough to drive away the unpleasant feeling for the rest of the evening. At most, we will gain another twenty minutes to half an hour.

The case of enjoyment and relaxation is no different from the other perceptions of life we have described in this part. Moreover, during our smoking life we become subconsciously conditioned in a way that completely prevents us from accepting our ability to go on and enjoy the evening without cigarettes as a realistic possibility. In any given situation this progression always leads to the same pattern of behavior, and as this conduct of ours continues the conditioning becomes increasingly entrenched.

We have created a vicious circle for ourselves of cause and effect, reason and result, and as long as this cycle is perpetuated the addiction becomes stronger and stronger. A powerful addiction is expressed in our perceiving reality as consisting of only one possible pattern of action, and this is the real meaning of an addict having his freedom of choice taken away from him. He is addicted to just one confined and compulsory way of behaving.

RELIEVING DISCOMFORT

Addiction is possibly the greatest contradiction to the concepts of freedom and choice, concepts that integrate very well with notions of enjoyment and relaxation. It is difficult to understand how the perception that apparently identifies pleasure and smoking came to be instilled within us since it is a perception that is so much the opposite of the real situation in which we find ourselves. The explanation for this is that temporarily preventing suffering by having a cigarette to relieve our discomfort is wrongly interpreted by us.

Indeed, the prevention of suffering is a comfort of some sort. There is a relief. But there is a big difference between relieving an existing state of distress – meaning an easing that gives us a feeling of relief from decreasing the level of distress – and actual genuine pleasure which expresses a real supplement that is not derived from the elimination of a shortcoming.

Imagine for a moment someone with a headache. With the pain gone after he has taken a pill, this person doesn't describe the experience of relief as a pleasure. The counteracting of suffering is a major benefit but is not perceived by us as being, in and of itself, a pleasure.

The problem of a mistaken definition in the case of cigarettes stems from the fact that we don't relate to our states and feelings in the periods in between one cigarette and another. During these periods when the nicotine begins to disappear from our body we move between various levels of discomfort up to feelings of real suffering. Since this is a reality that we have grown used to living with over a period of years, we don't define it in this way and simply ignore it.

Generally we also rush to relieve the feelings of discomfort by smoking yet another cigarette. This conduct focuses our attention on the relief we get from the cigarette, while completely ignoring the fact that it is the lack of nicotine which is the initiating cause of the problem in the periods between one cigarette and another. From here, the path ahead is cleared for us to define things wrongly without being at all aware that we are simply deceiving ourselves.

Every one of us who over the years taught himself to set in stone the mantra that links smoking with pleasure, has to ask himself 'can I, in my present state, act in any other way?' 'Do I have the choice of either enjoying myself with a cigarette or enjoying myself – perhaps a little less – without it?'

As long as the second widely held mantra 'I *must* have a cigarette' remains intact in all sorts of situations, it clearly signals the smoker's attempt to prevent unease or prevent suffering. If you feel that you 'must' have a cigarette and that if you don't the quality of your life will be diminished, you are in a very similar situation to that of the person who is trying to get rid of his headache, and it doesn't matter whether you acknowledge the truth and notice it or ignore it.

Don't delude yourselves into thinking that if you don't notice something this might be to your advantage. There is no advantage in this. A person who is deceived into thinking that he enjoys something that merely relieves his state of discomfort does not make his experience any different. The practical implication of this lack of discernment is merely that the behavioral conditioning is strengthened, which means that the addiction is becoming stronger.

CHAPTER 9

Appetite Suppressant and Digestive Assistant

Even though these are physiological phenomena that don't strictly belong to the area of our mental system, we will nevertheless relate to them here since they are included in the list of things that smokers describe as benefits from smoking. And so, in contrast to the previous issues in the list where it was important to re-examine our perceptions, when it comes to the issues of appetite suppression and assisting the digestive system, our physical senses do, in fact, represent a genuine reality.

When we note on the white board all of the benefits cited by the participants and then go through the list, we eventually draw a line through every topic mentioned. Thus a comprehensive picture emerges demonstrating that the wide range of assumptions we make about the various benefits to be had from smoking, conceals the fact that in each case smoking results in a loss of benefit rather than in a gain.

The only subjects that remain on the board without a line through them are smoking as an appetite suppressant and smoking as an assistant to digestion. At least these do not conceal the true reality as is the case with the others. Seemingly we have at long last found something related to this addiction to which we can attribute some sort of benefit. But here too we will come to realize that even in these matters we cannot hold on to the alleged benefit of smoking.

APPETITE SUPPRESSANT

Many smokers do indeed maintain the perception that smoking suppresses appetite and prevents them from putting on weight. I personally remember that while I was still a smoker I decided to go on a particularly strict diet and resorted to cigarettes to help me ease the feelings of hunger. To whoever asked me what my diet consisted of I would say that I was mainly eating cigarettes. Though this was of course a metaphor and I wasn't actually eating the cigarettes, the meaning of what I was saying was that I was smoking a lot and this prevented me from feeling hungry all the time. In everything concerned with easing the feeling of hunger, the cigarettes were for me a food substitute.

Nonetheless, the incontrovertible fact was that my overweight was accumulated during my years as a smoker. If smoking, like some sort of wonder drug, had been a real appetite suppressant, all smokers would be thin. Our bodies learn to adjust to the condition of smoking, and even though it has an influence on our feelings of hunger, over time our bodies develop a certain immunity to this particular influence.

The feeling of hunger is part of our natural craving processes and is essential to us. If we were to eat only when we felt hungry that would be excellent for us. We have to understand that overweight is mainly due to the fact that many of us eat even when we are not hungry rather than because we eat when we are hungry.

Culturally, a good appetite is perceived as a sign of health and strength. Appetite is not something that needs to be suppressed, so that the attempt to exchange the need for eating by increasing our cigarette consumption is not a particularly clever tactic nor is it effective, given our body's ability to adapt to the new condition over time.

People with a tendency to put on weight do not solve the problem by becoming smokers; those who were overweight before they took up smoking continue to be overweight also after they become smokers. There is a correlation between overweight and wrong eating habits, particularly eating when we are not really hungry, as well as the types of food we consume and the amount of physical exercise we do.

The reality of our being smokers actually makes it harder to maintain our proper weight because smoking disturbs the normal functioning of our body and makes us more sluggish and more tired. Our lungs are used to absorbing the smoke we inhale which results in a major decrease of our cardiovascular endurance. That is the reason why many of us breathe heavily even when doing minimal physical exercise. Nowadays it has already become a matter of common knowledge that smokers are reducing their physical fitness, and that a lack of physical exercise is one of the major causes of overweight, especially when people consume fatty foods and foods high in processed carbohydrates. Low levels of physical exercise make it difficult for the body to get rid of an excess of food. In other words, even if we have less appetite but we eat the wrong types of food and do little exercise, the result will be that we'll gain weight.

As always when we try to artificially influence the body system we are unable to achieve sustainable results. The attempt to use cigarettes as a way of keeping our weight down is nothing more than a feeble excuse for finding some sort of advantage in this addiction.

DEALING WITH A TENDENCY TO OVERWEIGHT

I definitely acknowledge the very genuine concern that smokers have of gaining weight as a result of quitting smoking. Some of you have even experienced this reality in the past, and there are even those who link their resumption of smoking to the increase in weight they experienced after their attempt to quit.

Quitting smoking can indeed be accompanied by a certain weight gain, but this is the place to emphasize that such an outcome is in no way inevitable. In fact, becoming free of smoking makes it possible to cope a lot more effectively with the tendency to put on weight for two major reasons. One is associated with our body's adjustment to the new state in which we have been cleansed of smoking and our body systems return to their natural way of functioning. What is important here is that we enable the body to return to its normal path. After years of constant smoking and the imposition of a heavy burden on the body due to the influence and overload related to cigarettes, we at long last give our bodies an opportunity to function in a natural way without any external influence.

If there is a tendency to gain weight it was there before, but now we can confront the problem and assess and analyze our situation in its true light. As long as we continue to smoke we don't really allow ourselves to observe our natural functioning. We have to remember that over the years and regardless of our being smokers, the functioning of our bodies changes as we age, and to this we have to add the effect of smoking cigarettes.

After years of smoking, during which we accustomed our bodies to function within the framework of certain specific conditions, we enable our bodies to regenerate themselves. Moreover, beyond the short period of adaptation to the new position, as our breathing improves and our blood vessels circulate more oxygen to all of the body's organs, we are able to produce much more energy and be a lot more active.

The second factor is concerned with the enormous emotional impact which is associated with the feeling of freedom we experience. Real freedom from smoking gained from a position of power, opens us up to a recognition of our great ability to shape our lifestyle according to what is good and right for us. In fact, our lifestyle as smokers was also shaped by us, each one of us for himself, except that we didn't consciously choose this and actually were dragged into reinforcing the situation day after day, year after year.

Thus we reached a level of addiction that reduced and greatly weakened our self-confidence also in such contexts as decisions and taking the initiative in shaping our lifestyles. We have already said that cigarettes intimidate us. When this condition is brought to an end we rediscover the fact that eating more properly, physical exercise, and choosing the types and quantities of food we consume, are all matters that are completely under our control.

And so it isn't a surprise to come across a friend of who has been set free of smoking and has suddenly also begun to eat more healthily and to be more active and vigorous. To the observer this sometimes seems strange even though it is a very logical process.

In general, smokers, exactly like non-smokers, are not afraid of displaying initiative and taking action energetically according to the objectives they wish to achieve. The unique obstacle of people who smoke revolves around their weakness in relation to smoking. It is a weakness that is reflected in various other mental and physiological aspects such as moods, tiredness, eating, physical exercise and the like. Thus when the obstacle of smoking is removed there remains no barrier or preventative factor in the way of self-awareness and the aspiration to live a better and more enjoyable life.

The notion of enjoyment, by the way, becomes very dominant also in this context since the set of rules relating to it also alters. No longer the dubious 'enjoyment' of the cigarette that claimed for itself an exclusivity which prevented us from enjoying many things for what they are, such as the real taste of food in meals, the real taste of coffee, physical exercise, breaks during the day, and countless other things.

Your lucky friends who quit smoking and overnight suddenly became keen advocates of a healthy lifestyle, didn't really go mad nor did they suffer from a mid-life crisis. All they did was to set free from the 'bear hug' of the cigarettes and that, in and of itself, is enough to create an opening and the motivation to get onto the path of the good life.

In a few more chapters, when you too embark on this new course and regain the good life, don't be surprised when you see that the change in your lives doesn't stop at just becoming free of smoking. Appetite comes with eating, and when we are set free from an addiction that so chains us and narrows our leeway, our drive to make changes and our sense of inner strength are tremendous.

A CHANGE FOR THE BETTER

Smoking doesn't suppress appetite but merely dulls the sense of hunger a bit in exactly the same way as it blunts the taste buds and sense of smell. These senses that over time weakened, return to being fully functional when we stop smoking. Following cessation, the experience of taste and smell strengthens as does the appetite. In the initial stages there is likely to be a slowdown in the body's metabolism and a tendency to eat more in order to reach a feeling of satiation. The period of adaptation we are talking about is, however, short and is followed by a natural return of our various senses to their normal and optimum state.

Since many smokers who approach quitting without the proper preparation are not aware of this information, they try to use eating as a substitute for smoking. Worse still, from a psychological perspective, they try to switch their daily activities with cigarettes, such as lighting up and smoking, to doing something else such as eating. The saddening outcome is weight gain and great frustration stemming from the false thought that this is the heavy and unavoidable price that has to be paid for quitting.

For many, this begins to sow a doubt as to whether this is a price worth paying. To the smoker who lacks both an understanding of the processes and proper instruction, this frustration joins a whole list of additional frustrations and the tendency is to start seeing every problem in life as stemming from quitting smoking. This is not a process of quitting and liberation from a pattern of activity and thought, but rather a process of self-condemnation which actually strengthens the old thinking patterns. And as the days pass, this turns into an inner war of arm wrestling between the prospect of being a grumbling and edgy non-smoker whose life is not a life, and a return to the smoking cycle and once more feeling miserable about those very same things that were initially the motive for quitting.

When we set out on a new course with a clear understanding that our lives are going to improve beyond recognition, we don't fear the minor changes of the first few days. All the feelings that indicate a change taking place within us – be they feelings of emptiness or a stronger sense of taste and a bigger appetite – confirm that something is indeed happening to us and that it is something good.

It becomes clear to us that our body is adapting to a new state and things will be back on track in a period that ranges between a few days and a few weeks. The process of setting free gets an incentive and a positive reinforcement every time we feel changes occurring within us. This is an important part of the process since throughout it we reconfirm to ourselves how great it is for us to be free.

When we have a proper understanding of the situation our starting point is totally different; what to others appears to be a minus is to us quite plainly a plus. Thus every difficulty we experience is understood by us to be part of a temporary price that we are paying for having at one time become smokers. We now understand that we have to go through a process of change so as to return our state to what it once was.

When we have changed our perceptions and come to understand that smoking is the unnatural state for us, and also that being free is the best and most rational way to be, every difficulty we experience is perceived by us as representing concepts from another world in which we used to live – a world we are now putting behind us.

A DIGESTIVE ASSISTANT

As for the assumption that smoking assists digestion; although the smoke does not become a part of our digestive juices, nicotine is considered a stimulant with an effect that is expressed, among other things, by an acceleration in our body's metabolism. Many smokers report an acceleration in their digestive system especially in the early hours of the morning, which results from the smoking of the first cigarettes of the day.

Here too it can be seen how we accustom our body to function in an apparently proper way only if we smoke. And if on a certain morning we don't smoke, the likely scenario is that our intestinal function will be slowed down and our abdomen will swell up. Moreover, this accelerated activity does not really reflect any proper functioning as it stems from a contraction of the blood vessels and intensified heartbeats. This is an excessive effort that is burdensome to the body and demands that it work harder.

Do you think that non-smokers have permanent problems with their digestion? Did we ourselves suffer from digestive problems before we became smokers? Certainly not. We also didn't notice this so called 'assistance' at the beginning of our smoking careers. The reason for this is that there wasn't any such assistance. Similarly to other aspects, this process of adapting the functioning of the body's digestive system to the effect of smoking is formed over time and gradually.

We do not need help with our digestion exactly as we don't need to suppress our appetite. What we do need is to reconcile the food we consume with our body's capacity. Also, in relation to the requirement in assisting our digestion, it has to be asked whether the problem lies in our body system or in prior causes that are, in fact, responsible for the digestive difficulties.

Foods that are not hard to digest and not overly processed, or foods that are consumed in the right combinations, will be well digested without any assistance. Only when we eat foods that are hard to digest and which our body finds it difficult to breakdown do we need help.

IGNORING THE SOURCE OF THE PROBLEM

Instead of paying attention to the real factors that are the cause of our problems, we sometimes develop a dependence on external means so as to get limited relief, and we regard this as being satisfactory. We have got used to using cigarettes so as to push the problem a little bit further on and gain time.

For anyone who nonetheless thinks that they have a unique digestion problem, let me point out that I have not yet come across anyone reporting a doctor's recommendation to take up smoking as a way of resolving such a problem. There are a wide range of pills and medications that are able to help at least as much, and in all probability a great deal more, than does smoking.

I can only try and imagine the scene of a person who goes to his family doctor, explains his digestive difficulties, and asks for possible solutions. The experienced doctor begins by saying: 'This is not that big a problem and there are today a range of possible solutions. I can give you a prescription for capsules or extracts. There are also many herbal remedies and tea infusions that do the job. It is of course preferable that we should take a look at the kinds of foods you consume and how you combine them, as it is most probable that they are the source of the difficulty.

Oh and yes, there is also another solution that I almost forgot to mention. If you really can't go with any of these options, you can always start to smoke cigarettes. This is a fantastic solution. Although at first it won't solve your problem because our body doesn't respond well to smoking, but if you persist with it and accustom yourself to the smoke and the smell, it will, in the end, speed up your metabolism.

The problem with this solution is that cigarettes are very harmful in many other ways and are also very addictive. So if you decide to smoke cigarettes in order to solve your digestive problem, take into account that from a physical and mental point of view you will become dependent on them. Oh yes, and another thing, most smokers can't control their cigarette consumption. As a result of the process of addiction it is reasonable to assume that you will be compelled to smoke a lot of cigarettes, and that actually most of the cigarettes you smoke will not be the ones you need to help you with your digestion.'

We have to acknowledge the truth of the reality; you and the millions of smokers around you don't smoke in order to assist your digestion or to suppress your uncontrolled appetite.

This extensive industry with a turnover in the billions which, on a massive scale, turns consumers all over the world into addicts, is not based on cigarettes performing as some sort of herbal medicine.

The true reason for this so unrestrained and disproportionate consumption when compared to any other product that we consume, is the addiction to nicotine which doesn't let us function normally without continuing to consume it during our daily routine.

The cigarette machines that are to be found in every town and on every street corner, and the convenience stores selling cigarettes, that are so widespread, are there because smokers are compelled to buy and smoke cigarettes every day – a matter in which from their point of view they have no choice.

Any average smoker who has finished a pack or is close to finishing it, hurries to the shop to replenish stocks while saying to himself or to the friend at his side 'I need cigarettes'. He doesn't say 'I have to maintain a normal digestion' or 'I have to suppress my appetite' or any of the other perceptions that we have already referred to.

The thinking pattern behind this saying is more general and represents the genuine basis of things – urge. An internal urge caused by the distress that results from a lack of nicotine. And when something pushes and distresses us, our response is general rather than specific, and the elementary saying will be 'I have to get rid of the disturbance' or in words more understandable to us 'I have to have a cigarette.'

One of the nice things is that in the period after setting free from smoking, when we allow the body to once again function in a normal way and without a dependence on cigarettes; all the systems stabilize, including our appetite and digestive system which come into line with the new reality.

Suddenly we begin to notice that we don't need special assistance with our digestion and we don't have to rely on external aids. All we needed was to allow our natural body systems to become active again, and enable them to function under regular and normal conditions without burdening them and without disturbing their normal rhythm.

When we feel better and our body's general functioning operates more smoothly, we become very aware of the change that has taken place and greatly enjoy the fact that this is directly related to our being set free from the dependency and the compulsion we experienced due to cigarettes.

CHAPTER 10

Aligning Thought and Action

The guiding principle in relation to our smoking, a principle which emerges over and over again in all of the thinking patterns that we form over the years, is that in the various situations we have described cigarettes are required in order to deal with a certain problem in our reality which was created within us by the addiction itself. The different situations in which we and many smokers like us identify 'benefits' are, in effect, all those situations in which the addiction brings us to the point where we cannot function adequately without cigarettes. We seemingly gain something from smoking, but all that 'something' comes down to is merely the ability to continue and function sufficiently well in our daily lives.

It is important that we understand how unfortunate this situation is. We consume a chemical compound called nicotine which enables us to feel fine only if we continue to consume it all the time. Meanwhile, in the breaks between one cigarette and another we feel constantly restless and uncomfortable. But because every smoker adopts a routine of smoking at more or less known intervals of time, we accustom ourselves to ignore these feelings of discomfort and not to relate them to our being smokers. The gaps of time between cigarettes tend to be such that we don't reach a point of real suffering in the in-between periods. Immediately when we begin to feel uncomfortable we take it as a clear sign that the need for another cigarette has been aroused within us, and we hurry to light another one and at once repress this feeling.

And yet, when we smoke and become temporarily at ease again, we give the cigarette full credit for this relief. This reality is interpreted by us as a gain from the cigarette and, in accordance with the situation in which we find ourselves at the time, we define for ourselves the kind of benefit we associate it with. Thus we create the perceptions that cigarettes relieve stress when we smoke in situations of tension; that they help us to pass the time while we wait or are bored; that they give us pleasure in situations of relaxation and leisure – situations in which we were supposed to enjoy ourselves also without them; that they give us self-confidence when we are in a social setting, and so on.

I pointed out earlier that we are deceiving ourselves, but it is important to make clear that this does not suggest that we do this intentionally. There is a great difference between the fact that smokers are being misled into thinking that cigarettes really help them, and a reality in which smokers are actually aware of this deceit. A person may be aware of the truth and still choose to ignore it and try to twist it, but our natural tendency is generally the reverse; we are unwilling to accept a situation in which we are aware of being misled.

For most of us the major obstacle is identifying the sham of cigarettes. And this is because what are perceived by us as benefits from smoking are situations in which the cigarettes do indeed give us real relief. The problem is that we are misled into thinking that this is a benefit we are getting from smoking, instead of understanding that this is a relief of a deficiency that only exists in a person who smokes.

There are smokers, particularly the younger ones, who truly believe that cigarettes give them a real advantage over non-smokers. This absurd belief stems from the human tendency to relate to the reality around us from our own personal perspective – 'If I don't function properly under pressure without cigarettes, then it would seem that this is also true for any other person.' And in the event that the 'other person' is a non-smoker and doesn't share the same perspective, then he is the one that is being deceived into thinking that he doesn't need a cigarette. Though such an approach is uncommon among most smokers, who don't generally think of their non-smoking friends as weak and inadequate, we can, nonetheless, learn something from this about the processes that influence our thinking.

THE NECESSITY TO CREATE A JUSTIFICATION

Generally, in our basic behavior thought precedes action. We are used to adapting ourselves to the surroundings we happen to be in; to whisper when we are in the cinema or in a theatre; to behave politely and respectfully when hosted by strangers; to obey traffic rules and traffic lights signals on the roads, and so on. Due to our awareness of our surroundings we exercise judgment in a way that best serves our interests. Only when our actions stem from instincts, extreme emotions or addiction, can a behavioral phenomenon that is not fully judgment based be discerned.

In the addiction to smoking the primary motive is based on physical feelings of discomfort and irritability. Smoking is a kind of relieving act, and even though we are not required to give explanations to anybody, still our thinking needs to be aligned with our actions.

We showed earlier that if we were to say to ourselves that smoking didn't really help us and that in fact it was nothing other than an act of self-deception that stems from an unpleasant physical feeling, clearly there would be a contradiction between the act of smoking and our thinking. This would make it very difficult for us to go on smoking. Therefore, though we don't say anything out loud, between ourselves we feel obliged to create a justification even for this action that stems from a compulsion. We must tell ourselves a story of some kind: 'I have to', 'it calms me down', and so on.

In fact, as mentioned above, we are not intentionally lying to ourselves. These are statements that describe the feeling that cigarettes give us in various situations. Except that these are explanations that we give to ourselves retrospectively. Meaning that we find ourselves lighting cigarettes all the time and in all sorts of situations, and accordingly we feel obligated to justify this reality. Moreover, since the experience returns by way of multiplication and repetition, so too the justifications perpetuate themselves and our thinking patterns become embedded.

This also explains why these mental conditions become so rooted. When the act of smoking is repeated over and over again in so many situations, together with the justifications we produce, a condition is created that says 'in these various situations you must have a cigarette': under pressure, while talking on the phone, at a meeting, at a social event, while studying, and so on. It is as if the lighting of a cigarette in these situations was a necessary condition for functioning properly.

This is how the world's most sophisticated drug achieves the objective of its various suppliers – to lead the user into such a level of dependence that he can only function normally when taking it. The picture of reality that the victim of the drug draws for himself is that without it the quality of his life would be seriously reduced.

The drug nicotine draws its strength from the simple truth that our thinking cannot tolerate a contradiction between it and our actions. Thus, so far as the cigarette manufacturers are concerned, it is enough to create a physical need that leads to the action of smoking. This action is combined with an almost imperceptible effect that doesn't interfere with smokers carrying out most daily assignments while taking the drug.

No more than this is required in order to create millions of addicts who, from the manufacturer's point of view, serve as human smokestacks that cannot imagine any other way of life other than with the drug. That is exactly how smokers appear to cigarette manufacturers.

This is not the sort of customer-supplier relationship that exists with any of the other products we consume. These suppliers don't need to improve the product or the service they provide to prevent the customer from turning to a competing product or giving it up completely. In the case of cigarettes the relationship is one of master and servant. The cigarette manufacturer knows that a starved smoker will search for his drug in the middle of the night even if he has to give up eating in order to get it. And even though cigarettes don't contribute anything to the body system and only burden it, they intimidate smokers and deny them rest.

The manufacturers' focus is the constant dissemination of more and more ads both explicit and implicit so as to sell a certain desired image to juveniles and adolescents so that they will be seduced into to the act of smoking. With the onset of the addiction, over time, the psychological justification will be created within every smoker – aligning the thinking with the action. To this day, the cigarette manufacturers try to broadcast to us messages of freedom, parties, pictures of exotic sites, a life of advancement and glamour – all of which are the very opposite of the true reality of the addiction.

However, in the face of the concealment and manipulation of the cigarette manufacturers, we now have the ability to put into practice a reality that is based on the very opposite approach – driving our actions to conform with our thinking. This for us is a key point, and the point of weakness of the cigarette distributors. By acquiring the knowledge as we have been doing throughout our reading till now, while at the same time becoming more aware of the processes we are experiencing, we have the power to take the reins into our own hands and change course.

Our insights in relation to the physical effects and the misconceptions that developed within us, enable us to embark on a new course of change based, henceforth, on actions that are aligned with our thinking and understanding. From here on we will focus on setting free from smoking in a practical way. It will become clear to us that all those retrospective thinking patterns that stemmed from the need to create justifications for the behavior imposed on us by the addiction, become meaningless when we are free. You will see how, from now, we will be able to utilize similar processes to those that created and reinforced the addiction in order to be set free of it forever.

Part Three:

Changing Course

CHAPTER 1

The Importance of Understanding the Process

We have so far been discussing the addiction from a number of different aspects. We have addressed matters regarding the process of the addiction's formation, the different influences on our body systems, and the manipulation that occurs in the areas of our behavior and thinking. We haven't at all dealt with the tools required to be set free from cigarettes and what has to be done in order for us to become smokefree. It is so for a reason and this formula exactly fits the structure of the meetings in the 'Smokefree way' program. The main process is the examination and close observation which we conducted through our conscious thought, as well as the fact that we related – most of us for the first time since we became smokers – to the processes that influence us and the way in which cigarettes gain control over our lives.

Usually when going through the kind of journey we have undertaken towards a safe exit from the smoking cycle, a number of interesting things happen to us along the way. The addiction, which was perceived by us as a kind of mysterious problem that at times it seemed we had no idea of how to even begin to deal with, now has a face and a shape and is much clearer and less threatening. We are no longer so intimidated by cigarettes and the threat that we would have to continue to smoke forever begins to seem less real.

Simultaneously, the readiness and motivation to make a change and set out on a new path increases. The motives for freeing ourselves from smoking are not only based on our having grown tired of being compelled to smoke all the time, but rather that a new aspiration has begun to develop within us – to return and experience life as non-smokers. And there is a real difference between this case and the feelings of misery that we had at the beginning of this journey. This is because the approach to embarking on a new course stems from a longing to achieve something new. We are already beginning to smell freedom.

From now on though, we will begin to deal with embarking on a new course and applying an actual change. However, all the tools and techniques that I will pass on to you won't work if you have not yet properly acquired the knowledge and awareness which this book offers. In other words, whoever leafed through the book and went straight to this chapter, thinking that quitting smoking depends only on actions and instructions without due preparation and an understanding of the addiction process, doesn't realize that setting free is a consequence and a direct continuation of diligent examination and close observation. These are the foundations, and when they are stable and clear setting free from smoking becomes a pleasant and joyful experience. On the other hand, without these foundations it is simply impossible to make a real change.

MERELY AN EXTERNAL PHENOMENON

Some of you are undoubtedly still somewhat bothered by the idea of actually stopping smoking and are, to some extent, stressed by the prospect that you may perhaps remain with a certain feeling of emptiness. This is mainly a fear of the unknown since for many years cigarettes have accompanied your lives every day and generally also for most of the day. You already no longer recall the reality of being in another state.

However, if you ignore this matter for a moment and assume that except for two or three days of very mild discomfort you are immediately embarking on a new path, and that your lives are being returned to be completely regular, without cigarettes, just as you were years ago and just as your non-smoking friends are now, then soon you will be among the happiest of people.

That is to say that if the dream comes true and suddenly without any difficulty your lives return to a natural path, that would be perfect. The coffee will be good and tasty also without an accompanying cigarette; telephone conversations and breaks will be pleasant just as they are, and situations of stress and social events will be totally fine and even more under control without cigarettes.

So the good news is that this is exactly how it is going to be. This is the big difference between someone who approaches making an actual change after the right preparation offered by the 'Smokefree way' program, and someone who tries to quit without any initial preparation or after improper preparation. The difference lies in the way in which we look upon the present and the future. And that difference is huge.

The exploration that we have undertaken throughout the book creates a change in the understanding of our connection to cigarettes and our actions with them. If in the past we perceived the reality of our lives as smokers as some kind of an act of fate because that fitted in with what we were actually doing now, after reviewing all matters we understand that despite the physical and mental hold it has on us, smoking is merely a phenomenon that is external to us and which has gained control over our lives in the course of time.

It becomes clear to us that we are first of all 'people' and not 'smokers'. Like all people, we live our lives and want to get the best out of them. Except that, unlike others, we have unintentionally subjugated ourselves and become addicted to the nicotine in cigarettes and have added smoking to the range of actions and routines in our lives.

The clear recognition that this whole addiction is external to us and forms no part of the substance of our personality, is in itself marvelous and possesses the great power to direct us to free ourselves from the addiction and begin to live our lives without dependence and without chocking, smelling bad, or enslaving ourselves. It is amazing just how simple the truth is, and how easy it is to grasp if things are properly understood.

Even before you have actually stopped smoking, the change as a result of reading the book and gaining the knowledge is already beginning to take place. Slowly, slowly, with each cigarette you smoke while thinking of smoking in and of itself, the act appears to be increasingly unreasonable and preposterous. This amounts to immense progress and suggests that the phenomenon of your smoking as you have known it is already in every sense losing its taste.

What remains for us to do is to cross the thin line that stands between us being actual smokers and becoming smokefree forever. We are talking about a very short process that is noticeable to us mainly only in the first two or three days, since these are the days during which we cross the border to a 'Safe Harbor'.

Although this initial period of your lives without smoking that is about to begin may concern some of you, since the dependence until now has been felt on a daily basis for years, when you set out on a new course you will suddenly see that your fear is based on nothing real. Even for someone who senses an emptiness and has a strange feeling while doing the usual things without a cigarette in hand – as with a hot drink, finishing a meal, breaks, and so on – it will all turnout to be a very temporary experience, at most an odd feeling but which involves no real distress.

In their first few weeks of being smokefree, many who have quit tell me that they can't understand how come it is proving to be so easy for them. And even more than this, also after a year without smoking ex-smokers who have been through the program tell me that they are still amazed that the transition was so smooth. Many repeat the same story: 'Tamir, I was a heavy smoker, a pack and a half a day; there was nothing I did without a cigarette. The change is so extreme and yet so smooth, I can't understand how, from the very beginning until today, cigarettes became for me so alien and uninteresting.'

To them it seems a wonder but to me it is all very clear. To be smokefree is dependent on the way we define ourselves. The moment we become aware that the dependence on cigarettes is a cycle in life that we ourselves are responsible for creating without in any way intending to, it becomes very easy for us to remove it from our lives – so much so that within a short time it seems to us as if it had never been there.

This is also the reason why we sometimes meet people who were at some time smokers and, once they had finally quit, became such strong opponents of smoking. Their smoking friends find this difficult to accept. They wonder how it is possible that someone who just until recently was a fellow smoker, suddenly within a short space of time loses all interest in smoking. What happened to him that isn't happening to them? They ask.

And there is also the more extreme version of somebody who was a heavy smoker and not only was freed from smoking but has become a nuisance to the community of smokers he has left behind. He doesn't stop criticizing and harassing smokers telling them that he can no longer abide the smoke and the repellent smell of their cigarettes. This already really annoys some of the smokers who say 'All right then, you have stopped smoking – well done, but to go to such lengths and become a missionary against smoking? That is too much.'

THE PRESENT OCCUPIES THE ENTIRETY OF OUR CONSCIOUSNESS

What lies behind these phenomena is the fact that each time we make a change our behavioral habits become embedded within the new state fairly quickly. Our brain is built to adjust rapidly to new conditions in which our behavioral pattern changes. All we have to do is to persist in the actions and repeat them over a period of two to four weeks in order to entrench the new reality. This is a process of adaptation

– meaning that we accustom ourselves to a new state while completely abandoning the previous set of conditionings.

In the event that things are based on an accurate process and proper preparation, our patterns adapt to the change so that the previous assumptions are no longer valid and no longer have the right of existence because they are simply no longer needed. Therefore, except for the initial period during which the change is being implemented and is felt by us as such, all we are left with after this is the present. The things we do daily.

We must pay attention to the fact that the reality of our being smokers occupied the entirety of our consciousness. We reached a stage at which from our point of view it seems as if we have always been smokers, so that our life experiences in those periods when we hadn't yet touched cigarettes have become insignificant. This is despite the fact that we once did everything in our lives without smoking. We didn't smoke during trips, when with friends, during breaks, while on the phone, with coffee, working at the computer, watching television, and so on.

We can also mention the examples of those of us who were totally against smoking until they themselves began to smoke, or the examples that our acquaintances sometimes remind us, of how we once led a more sporting life and were so unconnected to smoking.

Exactly in the same way as we have already forgotten how it once was, so too our being smokefree is about to occupy the entirety of our awareness. Then, to us as non-smokers, it will also seem strange to think that we were smokers in the past.

The structure of our thinking is simply built to work in this way and to be affected mainly by the given situation in the present after adapting a new lifestyle. Therefore, it is not surprising that ex-smokers get so quickly used to being smokefree and behave as if they don't have many years of smoking behind them. It's not that they forget that they once smoked, they don't. But they no longer experience reality as smokers, they live with a feeling of freedom and cleanliness, and the experiences of the past simply become meaningless in the light of their current state of being. And the big bonus here is that this won't take a few years or even months. All it requires is just a few weeks.

For a significant number of people, the first days of being set free from smoking turn into some kind of corrective experience and there are others for whom these days turn out to be just a kind of game. It is an opportunity to see life and experience it without smoking knowing that all the feelings surrounding these days are also a one-off experience. This is because very quickly the new lifestyle will become entrenched and within a short period we will no longer feel anything special.

Though the experience of crossing the border into a 'Safe Harbor' is like a trip into the unknown, it is merely a trip toward a complete life in which the notion of 'smoking cigarettes' remains no more than a memory of a distressing period of our history and nothing more.

THE FLAW IN ATTEMPTING TO QUIT WITHOUT PROPER PREPARATION

Contrary to the above, smokers who attempt to quit without acquiring the necessary knowledge and awareness are not, in fact, changing any aspect of their perception. In their self-definition they remain 'smokers' whilst in practice they are trying to stop the act of smoking. Assuming they succeed in abstaining from smoking for a while we can call people in this situation 'smokers on a break'.

A small minority of them will perhaps persist in their abstinence for some time, but for the vast majority the fate of this break, in accordance with the meaning of the term 'break', is that it will come to an end and the smokers will return to their old ways.

This way, the time factor also works against those who stop, because in all sorts of life situations they remind themselves of how much they are missing cigarettes. These smokers are not setting themselves free of the smoking addiction but only from actually smoking cigarettes for a while.

From the period when I myself was a smoker, I remember coming across another smoker who tried to stop in this way and found it quite important to declare to me: 'Look, I'm only stopping for a while; I will go back to smoking in the future.' He thus found a way of reassuring himself that he was not giving up on his beloved cigarettes forever but merely temporarily separating himself from them.

I too was unable at the time to recognize the absurdity of this approach. If a person wants to change something in his lifestyle, it is supposedly out of a recognition that making such a change would be a more correct way for him to lead his life and better for him in every respect. This is similar to what we said about being on a trip and choosing a direction that didn't lead to the destination we wanted to reach. If we clearly realize that we are going in the wrong direction, we immediately turn around and go back retracing our footsteps without any qualms about doing so. There are no conflicts or doubts on this. We don't say 'I will one day return to this road that doesn't take me to where I want to go.' That would be preposterous. However, when we are talking about cigarettes on which the smoker has become so dependent, he doesn't understand that this dependence stems from a weakening of his self-esteem rather than some gain in the cigarette. He then has to tell himself a story and leave an opening of sorts for the hope that the period of 'misery' he has condemned himself to, will also end at some stage.

This illustrates the huge difference between someone who approaches quitting through an understanding of the addiction, a strong desire to set free from it and to create a new lifestyle, and someone who tries to stop smoking because he feels that he cannot continue to suffer any longer but has no understanding of the fact, not even the most basic, that real change cannot be achieved unless we first rationally question our basic assumptions in relation to smoking.

CHAPTER 2

Changing Course

Now that our starting point is based on the review we have engaged in so far, from here on we are embarking on a new course toward our freedom. It follows a path that greatly resembles the process of addiction itself, except that it is a reverse process – through the physical effect and the effect on our subconscious.

Immediately with the actual cessation of smoking – to which we will soon relate in detail – we begin to cleanse our bodies. Over a long period of time our body systems got used to our being smokers and adapted themselves to function with the presence of the drug nicotine. From the moment we begin to cleanse our bodies these systems have to adapt themselves again to functioning without the burden of smoke and nicotine.

Even though for us this change is an excellent one, the fact is that with every change in an existing state our body responds and sends us signals that something is not as usual. These signals are the physical feelings we will experience as a result of cutting off the supply of nicotine to the body. This can remind us of the addiction experience itself. Then too, when we started to allow nicotine into our body it sent us messages. These were messages of rejection and the responses were bouts of coughing, a sore throat, dizziness and, at times, other unpleasant occurrences.

This time round the sensations will be a lot milder and expressed chiefly in a feeling of slight emptiness. Sometimes these feelings are so mild that some of those who are quitting are not at all aware of them. Once the period of smoking in our lives comes to an end our body immediately ceases to be attacked by smoke and is also required to devote fewer resources in order to deal with the presence of nicotine. Because of this the period of adaptation by the body is also very short and lasts for no more than two to three days.

Actually this brief process is not exclusively based on the body's adjustment. Our body never came to terms with the presence of the nicotine and the smoke so that also during our lives as smokers, in all the lulls between one cigarette and another, as well as while we are asleep, our body is trying to cleanse the system as much as possible. What happens in the first days of cessation is that the cleansing takes place continuously over the entire period including those times when we are asleep as well as when we are awake and fully conscious.

The heart of the process is, to a large extent, linked to our consciousness becoming adjusted to the new state in which the body regulates itself to function as usual – and the emphasis here is on the words as usual – without the presence of the drug nicotine. Since a change is taking place we feel it to a certain extent, meaning that we are aware of it. Yet within a few days our consciousness becomes used to the situation and we feel it less and less.

This is what also happened with the addiction itself: we had sore throats and dizziness, we were very much aware of these unpleasant feelings, until the body adjusted itself to function in as reasonable a way as possible in conjunction with our smoking, and our consciousness learned to ignore the chocking, the bad taste and the smell. The body adjusts its functioning to any situation and the consciousness falls into line with it.

Whoever once bought glasses with a differently sized frame from his previous pair, surely remembers that in the first few days every time he put them on, no matter in what direction he turned, he couldn't avoid noticing the new frames – something which at the time was a bit distressing. What happens after a few days is that our brain learns to focus our vision in a forward direction and thus ignore the frame. This is done without it being noticed and without trying to train ourselves to reach such a point. This is precisely what is about to happen to us within a few days of the moment we set out on the new nicotine-free course.

THE PROCESS OF MULTIPLICATION AND REPETITION

Though setting out on this pathway is indeed the beginning of the process, the most significant change of course, and the one that will lead us to be completely smokefree, takes place over a slightly longer period. We are talking about taking the same route along which the addiction was created except that this time we go in the opposite direction – the way out.

We all know that youngsters who experiment with the first cigarettes in their lives do not feel addicted in just a few days. Even though the disruption of balance and the physical need develop very quickly, nonetheless over a period of weeks and sometimes even months, these youngsters do not identify themselves as smokers but only as people who are experimenting with smoking for the fun of it. They can certainly get to a restaurant and sit in the non-smoking area, and they are not yet able to smoke on a daily basis or in quantities resembling those of an average smoker of a pack a day.

What mainly typifies this period is that these youngsters are in an in-between state in which they see themselves as being, in effect, occasional smokers, but definitely not as 'smokers' by their own self-definition.

Even though they are not aware of it, they have already begun a process that, after they have persisted over a period of time in smoking, will necessarily turn them into smokers by definition. And this happens – to remind you – because as long as we consistently act in a certain way and repeat it time and again, the action shifts from our conscious mind to our subconscious and over time becomes second nature to us.

So it is also with our setting free from being smokers; the main issue is latent in our self-definition, and this definition does not only depend on what we consciously say to ourselves, but is to a large extent very dependent on our subconscious.

We cannot turn directly to our subconscious – as this is a part of our personality that is not directly influenced by our insights and knowledge. It can only be formed and defined by one kind of process – multiplication and repetition. All we have to do from the moment we embark on a new course and cease to smoke in practice is to continue with our lives as usual, but pay attention to the fact that with every action we execute we reinforce with one more layer our new reality as smokefree people.

When we get up in the morning and drink a cup of coffee, despite the strange feeling during the first days, we need to understand that every time we rise in the morning and every cup of coffee we experience without a cigarette, repeats once more what happened on the previous day. Our brain is designed to absorb this recurrence of actions without cigarettes in exactly the same way as it recorded the multiplication and repetition of the smoking act during the process of addiction.

So it turns out that in setting ourselves free of the smoking addiction we use the very same technique that led us to become smokers. This is expressed in every ending of a meal without a cigarette, every phone conversation without smoking, every lunch break that we take advantage of to breathe some fresh air, to drink something, and simply enjoy the break for its own sake. Every time we take the same actions without smoking, the very same actions we were accustomed to taking with a cigarette, we are sending a message to the subconscious – this is our new lifestyle.

We are also used to explaining this in the following way: The addiction is like a thick rope wrapped around us. As is known, a thick rope is made out of many thin strands that are intertwined and curled until they become one thick, strong unit. The strands themselves are thin and weak but when bound together they can create an extremely strong rope.

Metaphorically speaking, the addiction to smoking is also composed of small components, those small daily actions that we carry out holding a cigarette. When we repeat these actions over and over again, they become as one in our subconscious. Therefore, in order for us to undo this sturdy rope we need to untie the bond that connects all the individual components.

This is achieved by the multiplication and repetition of our daily actions without smoking so that every action leads to the untying of one more strand and then another of our previous behavioral patterns.

Seemingly we are not actively doing anything special, because what happens is that we stop smoking and continue with our lives as usual only without lighting up. This is indeed one action less and therefore the verbal definition is usually 'I am a non-smoking person', which means there is a certain action I don't perform.

But I would actually like to propose looking at it from a different viewpoint. For us as new non-smokers we are, indeed, doing something special in all the situations in which we don't smoke. For us, especially during the first few weeks, the fact that we finish meals, have phone conversations, hold meetings, go on trips and do many other things without smoking, has something very active about it.

This is not only a matter of refraining, but rather an active performance of the very same things in a way that is different to what we have been used to till now. It is important for me to clarify that this is not merely a matter of semantics. The very fact that we notice that something is happening here, that every action is a further reinforcement of the process of multiplication and repetition, will greatly help us to progress. This is so because as time passes and the number of actions performed according to the new course we are on mount up, our smokefree state is enhanced both at the subconscious level as well as at the conscious level.

In this way the passage of time works in our favor. Each day and each hour are not difficult moments that we have to get through and survive, but the very opposite. Every period of time and every action we perform in life are the working tools that enable us to undo the old behavioral patterns.

When we started to smoke we shaped a lifestyle of constant smoking because we weren't aware that each cigarette strengthens and thickens the noose of the addiction around us. Now, however, we're proceeding clearly aware of what we are doing – albeit in precisely the opposite direction – multiplying and repeating all our regular daily actions without cigarettes. With no particular effort and without changing our everyday life, this course will very quickly lead us to being completely smokefree.

In this context I have a small confession to make to you. I am a 'heavy non-smoker'. I don't smoke approximately two packs a day. The reason I see things in this way stems from the fact that every day, just as you do, I bump into so many smokers. There is smoking all around us, in the street, outside shopping malls and office buildings, in some restaurants, as well as in a wide range of other places. For me all those smokers are a very pleasant reminder of the fact that I am now a non-smoker.

It is wonderful to be a heavy non-smoker. I get to enjoy each and every cigarette that I don't smoke, and I am very happy to see myself balanced and calm in all of life's situations without holding a cigarette. I am also not required to have a break every time I don't smoke a cigarette. I smell great and enjoy an excellent sense of smell, my taste buds work better, and this doesn't even cost me any money. But the most enjoyable part of being a heavy non-smoker is the feeling of freedom. I am no longer enslaved to cigarettes or to the companies that manufacture them, and I no longer feel that I am being pulled along by something over which I have no control or power to decide.

I have not lost the 'cool' feeling that there once was in cigarette breaks. I still meet up with smokers and go out for a chat with them in the open air while they smoke and I don't. I have also not become more limited from a social point of view or come to despise smokers. On the contrary, it has become one of my objectives in life to help people exit the smoking cycle and join me in my new found place. Being a 'heavy non-smoker' is not merely a definition to draw attention, but is indeed a tangible reality that characterizes the feelings of pleasure that are to be had every time we come across a reminder of our being smokefree.

THE TRANSITION TO ADAPTING A NEW LIFESTYLE

Our body has the ability to function like a very advanced washing machine. The extent to which the human system is geared to continuous self-repair is astonishing. With cessation of smoking there immediately begins a process of the cleansing of all the organs. Our lungs drain out all the dirt that has accumulated in them, oxygen very quickly and easily begins to circulate to all the organs, the taste and olfactory receptors return to functioning much better, and in general we become more energetic.

All of this happens the minute we embark on the new course. The amazing thing is that within just a few weeks the body will have almost completely cleaned out all the poisons inside it. In this context, by the way, those quitting who experience an increase in coughing and discharge of phlegm during this period, are exhibiting a good sign evidencing the fact that the body is doing what it is supposed to do. This doesn't happen to everyone because of natural functional differences between people, but whoever does experience such symptoms should know that these are an excellent sign of the cleansing process. It is highly likely that the reason this takes place specifically during smoking cessation is connected to the fact that the body is not ready to cleanse the surpluses so long as a person smokes on a regular basis. But from the moment the burden of systematic smoking is lifted, it is as if the body is able to recognize this and is more prepared to force out the poisons.

Similarly, the mental system is also designed to adjusting itself to the adoption of a new lifestyle within a few weeks. In whatever is connected to life's daily routine, our brains are set to rely mainly on the short term memory in transmitting messages to the subconscious. Maintaining a certain new behavioral pattern for a month is enough for it to become established.

We usually clarify this in meetings of the 'Smokefree way' program with a number of examples. Let's assume that in the street in which you live the municipality decides to invest in developing the neighborhood. When the work on infrastructure is completed the whole street assumes an entirely new appearance with the roads and pavements having been renovated and completely changed.

Even the exit from the house or building you live in has changed. If you are used to going out to work every day by foot or in a car by turning in a particular direction, these pathways are the opposite of what they have been till now. The road has become one way and going out by car obliges you, for instance, to turn right and take a route encircling the street instead of exiting the car park by tuning left as you always did in the past. The same thing applies if you are on foot. From now on you have to turn right instead of exiting the house and going left along the pavement.

Even if we assume that the change is for the better and significantly shortens the travel time by car or on foot, habits are still habits and they tend to linger, at least for a while. Every time we leave the house during the first days after the change, our tendency will be to do what he had got used to doing for years before then. If on foot, this can mean walking dozens of yards as you set off until you suddenly remember. The response will usually be 'Oh yes, I forgot. This is no longer the right way, in a bit the way ahead will be blocked.' And you have no choice other than to go back and return to the new road. In a car this can even be a little bit dangerous because you might find yourself actually travelling against the traffic.

In any case, what in practice happens to us is that even if we make a mistake the first few times, we quickly align ourselves with the new reality. The tendency – which is an indication of the subconscious – the very thought that is driven by the routine, quickly becomes a new routine – to go along the new road that has been paved for us in the street.

Sometimes it is actually possible to discern in the course of the first few times – whilst we still haven't internalized the change – that something nonetheless alters between one mistaken turn and the next. On the first occasion we went quite a few yards until we remembered that this was not the right way. Second time round we had only taken a few steps until we woke up to the fact that we had taken a wrong turn and go back.

Every time we leave the house and take the new way, whether we had been mistaken previously or had already got used to the change, each such occasion reinforces the new routine. Our brain passes on the message from our conscious thinking – that the road has changed – to our subconscious thinking – that we have to turn right instead of left. This is constructed by the accumulation of the number of times through multiplication and repetition of the action of leaving the house. This has to happen in a consistent way between twenty to thirty times in all, in order for the subconscious thinking to fall into line with our actions.

Without paying any special attention to this, we constantly make changes in patterns and our life's routine. Practically every external change in life's routine necessitates a modification of behavioral patterns. This can relate to a change in our workplace involving a move of our offices from one floor of the building to another, when the tendency during the first few days is to press the lift button for the wrong floor. Or, for example, when switching the computer's operating system and finding it difficult to activate applications that have been changed because we are so used to operating in a particular way. Even changing the remote control of the cable company can result in us pressing the wrong keys due to old habits. The same is also true when we change over to new electrical devices or a new car.

I had the good fortune in the past to go on a backpackers trek to New Zealand. In order to explore its two fascinating large islands, my partner and I bought an old vehicle in good condition that served us well throughout the trip. As is known, New Zealand is a member of the British Commonwealth and as a result the traffic flows in reverse to the way it does in many countries in the world. In principle the rules are no different, but you drive on the left and not on the right hand side of the road.

For someone who comes from a country where you drive on the right, this makes it seem as if you are entering, say a roundabout, the wrong way. The same goes for the build of the car when the driver's seat and the wheel are on the right hand side of the vehicle instead of the left.

You would have thought that drivers coming from various places in the world would be required to undergo some sort of instruction before being allowed to drive, and yet it turned out that my international driving license was valid and I could start driving immediately. Even though we are talking about travelling on the roads of a foreign country and there is a risk of road accidents, it seems that the countries involved put their trust in the fact that a driver who has to accustom himself to flows of traffic that are the reverse of what he is used to will, of necessity, be more alert and careful with his driving.

I can well remember the first few times I had to enter a roundabout, saw the cars in front of me, and thought to myself: 'wow, what are they doing? They are entering the roundabout the wrong way, have they all gone mad?' No, they were not going the wrong way and I too quickly came to my senses and merged into the traffic exactly as they had done. My immediate inclination was to interpret the scene facing me on the basis of years of driving in another country. But because I was attentive and alert I quickly remembered that I was in a new place and adapted my driving to the changed reality. Within a few weeks I was already used to driving on the left and had completely forgotten that for years I had been accustomed to driving on the other side of the road.

Our brain assimilates the new actions that recur every day, and when the new behavior is repeated in an identical way over a period of time, taking it in no longer requires conscious attention and awareness, and the actions shift to being carried out subconsciously.

Surprisingly, when I returned home and started to drive in accordance with the traffic direction I had once been used to, it seemed strange and required me to get used to it once again. But this time the process of adaptation was far quicker because the previous patterns had not been erased from my subconscious but were simply dormant. To re-awaken patterns acquired in the past that had simply not been active for a while is an even faster process than acquiring new ones.

You will soon set off on the new course you want so much to be on. The actual change will occur by persistently carrying out your routine actions when free of the need to conduct your lives while holding a cigarette. But don't make the mistake of thinking that this is no more than merely a technique, for there could not be a greater mistake.

The foundations of the process are based on the perception that you are changing. Only because of that can you perform the routine tasks of life acknowledging and gaining satisfaction from every act. You are indeed cancelling out a need that you created. In the coming days and weeks every lunch that ends without a cigarette will be added to more and more lunches that end in this way. After two, three, five, and ten times consecutively, the natural feeling at the end of the meal will be excellent and the inclination to light up after eating will simply disappear.

So it will also be when drinking coffee without a cigarette, during breaks, and in everything else you do. Every such action is yet one more occasion when we apply the new behavioral pattern. Every time you feel that something is different you can say to yourselves: 'This is one more occasion when I have finish eating or drinking coffee, or had a phone conversation, and so on, without smoking.'

Although this process of eliminating a need does indeed involve an adjustment to behavioral patterns that are not controlled by conscious thinking but rather belong, in fact, to the subconscious, without preparation, observation, and an understanding of the process, performing the actions themselves wouldn't have any value.

You are approaching a practical process which essentially does not require any special effort. Simply by your being persistent and the passage of a relatively short period of time will see to it that a new reality becomes entrenched and that you are set free of smoking forever. However, it is not at all possible to talk about anything practical without the advance preparation that you have undertaken and the understanding that you have acquired.

It can be said that you had to follow the long path of observation and change of perception in order to reach the stage of actually putting it into practice. And when you get to that stage well prepared, all that remains is to embed your new perception as smokefree by persistently transmitting the messages to the subconscious.

CHAPTER 3

The Same Effort

It is very much worth your while to memorize the phrase 'the same effort'. To completely stop smoking is a process that is no more difficult than starting to smoke. For most people who do this in the right way, it in fact turns out to be much easier. In any case, we can confidently say that the required effort if not easier is, at the very least, the same as the effort that was required to become a smoker.

Smokers are quite naturally particularly concerned about the first few days when they will have to cope with the new situation awaiting them. At this stage some occasionally say to me: 'I am ready to make a change and really want at long last to experience being smokefree, but Tamir, getting through tomorrow and the following day is really troubling me.'

Not everyone feels that way. In my own quitting I, for example, was less troubled than that. I was really interested by then in putting my life back on the right track. I was very focused on the anticipation of seeing how my life would change so that instead of being a person who all the time felt he had to have something, I would become a person who didn't have that feeling of compulsion. It excited me to see how this happens.

Indeed, as it is for every smoker, I had my apprehensions whether everything would be OK and that I wouldn't find myself climbing the walls. But in any case I thought it was right to approach my smoking cessation with a level of confidence that, as much as possible, resembled the confidence with which sixteen years earlier I had started to smoke.

For some reason, when we were younger and experimented with the first cigarettes in our life, we were not worried about the early days of adjusting to smoking. As we saw it, the process was a challenge. The difficulties of a sore throat and stinging eyes, coughing, chocking, dizziness, bad smell and a terrible taste, all of these didn't stand in the way of us realizing the experience and feeling adult and cool.

We didn't have even the slightest fear that we would become addicted smokers and that ahead of us were many years of being enslaved and weighed down – physically, mentally and economically. We were very focused on experiencing this rite of passage, and as we persisted and adjusted ourselves to the discomfort involved in smoking we felt that we had gained something. Finally we stopped coughing, learned to inhale all the way into the lungs, and the taste and smell became less and less noticeable.

We had no fear whatsoever of venturing into the 'unknown', toward a new reality that would change our lifestyles and oblige us to adjust the entire schedule of our day around this 'strange activity' – which was our way of perceiving the act of smoking when we first began.

We didn't take into account that as a result of this initial experience we would have to go out for many cigarette breaks every day; that we would always need to make sure that we had a pack and to take stock every day of the number of cigarettes we had left; that we would have to develop orientation skills whenever we arrived somewhere enabling us to find the areas where smoking was allowed; and that we would bring upon ourselves absurd situations such as driving in a car with the window slightly open when it was raining, or give up on the air conditioning at the height of summer, or finding ourselves outside the house in the freezing cold of winter, all in order to get another dose of nicotine into our bloodstream.

I usually remind worried participants of these things and ask why we shouldn't feel a similar confidence about the path we are now adopting on our way toward smoking cessation. After all, the way is the same way; this is what is so great about the 'Smokefree way' program, it's just that we are now heading in the opposite direction.

Indeed, when we started to smoke at least most of us were young and unaware of the implications of this experience, whereas now we are approaching the change out of a clear awareness and understanding. This is the difference between going to a place that is good for us and is based on a rational view of reality, and going to a place that is good for the cigarette manufacturers. The latter is based on completely ignoring the expected results, and occurs entirely because of the lack of awareness of youngsters and the vanity that is typical of adolescence.

In the same way that the first few days of our experiencing the effect of smoking were strange and required an effort by us to deal with phenomena that we were not used to, so too the exit to free ourselves from smoking necessitates dealing with a few days of feeling an emptiness and perhaps a few days of restlessness. But this challenge is no less exciting and an experience no less interesting.

Because we are not talking here of absolute equivalence between the two efforts, the concept of 'the same effort' relates more to intentions rather than it being a description of reality. Coping with the difficulties of smoke, the chocking and the coughs, was incomparably more difficult than what you are about to experience in the first two or three days of cessation. The essence of this concept is that it is appropriate for us to be willing to make an effort to free ourselves from smoking, in a way that is at least equal to the effort we were prepared to invest in order to become smokers.

We set off in the knowledge that this is an experience that provides closure not only by definition but also practically. In the brief period that we will go through in the first few days we will be fixing our lifestyle, regularizing our physical conduct and breathing, and allowing ourselves to at long last taste freedom. This is an incomparably more exciting aim than the goal that led us years ago to smoke – the misconception that with cigarettes we would be 'cool' and more adult.

The timeframe relating to the two directions is also not equal. The process of addiction is very imperceptible and most smokers don't notice it at all during the first months. The dependency on smoking, that begins to develop after just a few days, doesn't change the fact that novice smokers don't notice their new state for some time and they convince themselves all the while that they are in control.

On the other hand, those who have just quit, immediately feel the desired change and are very happy and surprised to discover that the dependency is a lot weaker that it at first seemed. Suddenly, you get up in the morning and enjoy sitting at the kitchen table or in the yard with just a cup of coffee in your hand and feel perfectly fine with it.

Contrary to the process of addiction, the feeling of freedom reflects a genuine reality. With that comes an excitement that we are really doing it, and not just that it is possible but also that it is wonderful. And this in contrast to the lie that accompanies the first period of addiction during which youngsters tend to hold on to the saying 'I can stop whenever I want to.'

To stop smoking is no more difficult, no more complicated, or requires any more of an effort than starting to smoke. Now that you have a clear understanding and awareness, it is going to be a lot easier. Exactly as we were prepared to make an effort to become smokers, there is no reason why we should not be prepared to make the same effort to become smokefree.

CHAPTER 4

Learning to Ride a Bike

There is one last point I want to clarify before we get to the practical act of quitting, and it is about a personal story that happened to me when I was nine. For some reason my parents forgot to teach me to ride a bike when I was younger. My father suddenly remembered that I was already a big boy and that it wasn't right that I had still not learned how to ride. I also felt that way and I was very excited when he took me to the neighborhood shop and bought me a shiny metallic Bordeaux BMX bike with yellow wheels and handlebars.

True, I couldn't ride my bike from the shop to my house, but the next day my father took me to an open area of the playground and began to teach me. It wasn't possible to attach auxiliary wheels to a bike for a nine year old, so my father had to teach me to ride in one go without aids and without it being done progressively. He instructed me to sit on the bike and grip the handlebars, while he stood at my side and held on to the underside of the seat with one hand and with his other hand joined me in grasping the handlebars. Once his grip had stabilized the bike he asked me to lift my legs up from the ground, put each on its pedal, and start pedaling.

After a few rounds like this, and after I had built up some confidence, my father slightly released his grip. At first he let go of his hold of the seat and then also removed his hand from the handlebars. From that moment on it was just me and the bike. What excitement! There I was riding a bike for the first time in my life. It's amazing how such small achievements can lift our spirits, especially in childhood.

Of course, despite the great excitement, it only took a few more seconds for me to lose my balance and both I and the bike crashed to the ground. My father encouraged me to get up and try again and after a few attempts, and a few more falls, I was able to keep the balance while still on the move, and each time managed to travel a little bit further before I once again fell. Indeed, it is not easy to learn to ride a bike in one go at the age of nine. Nonetheless, despite the frustration of repeatedly falling, the joy of riding the bike, even for just a few seconds each time, spurred me to continue trying until I gained complete control of it.

There was one problem I was unable to deal with – I had great difficulty in keeping the handlebars stable. Every time I steered in a certain direction I immediately would try and correct it by steering too far to the other side. So I found myself struggling with the handlebars; first to the right, then to the left, too far to the right again, and then once more to the left until finally I fell to the ground. My father, who was observing me from the sidelines for about half an hour, noticed this, came up to me and said 'Tamir you are beginning to cycle very well and managing to keep the bike stable, but there is one thing you are not doing right. You are looking instinctively at the handlebars and the front wheel and this is causing you to occasionally lose balance. Try looking a few yards ahead. Even if you need to turn right or left, keep on looking ahead instead of at the handlebars and you will see that you will be able to stabilize the bike without a problem.'

So I did what he suggested and began to ride the bike smoothly without any falls. However strange it seemed to me at the beginning not to look at all at the handlebars, I understood after a while that in fact when I began to look ahead I stopped narrowing my field of vision to just the handlebars and the front wheel – something which had made me respond with movements that were too sharp and made me lose my balance. On the other hand, by widening my field of vision my movements became steadier and more proportionate in relation to the road while at the same time maintaining stability. I learned to ride within a short time and to this day enjoy occasional trips on road bikes.

LOOKING AHEAD

How I learned to ride a bike was something I remembered while I was myself in the process of quitting smoking. Sometimes, when we are experiencing a new state, we have a tendency to perceive things narrowly and relate to the situation in a way that is not proportional, like our natural tendency when first learning to ride a bike to look at the handlebars and the front wheel.

Soon, when you get through the first few days, when you might possibly have feelings of emptiness or restlessness, it is important that you lift your head up and look a few yards ahead. Think two or three weeks ahead. Our feelings during the first few days are for sure more intensely sensed because we are accustoming ourselves to a new state. But by looking more broadly ahead at the timeline, in a few weeks, the whole period of years of smoking will all be behind us. Therefore, when looking at a point in time a few weeks hence, even if as you do so there are feelings of discomfort, these feeling are seen in proportion and become simpler and easier to accept.

The major fears about stopping to smoke revolve around our having to deal with feelings of stress and emptiness. You need to acknowledge that life goes on as usual during the first few days of cessation. You will go to work as usual, do the shopping, run errands, and fulfill all your other tasks. If there are feelings of restlessness we're talking about a feeling that altogether lasts for just a few seconds. There could, for example, be a stressful telephone conversation during which you will feel a little bit less relaxed than usual, or a feeling of stress for a few seconds that might be expressed by excessive sweating.

All these, if they are felt at all, are episodes that quickly fade away. The problem with these symptoms is not in the symptoms themselves. These are merely quick flashes that pass of their own accord, or can be eased by stopping for a moment and taking a few deep breaths or drinking half a glass of water. Only if we look narrowly at a certain symptom and turn the feeling into something much bigger than it really is, are we likely to miss the point and our responses can then be more extreme.

A feeling, whatever that feeling may be, can be accepted by us as an experience that we have to go through, which makes it possible for us to absorb it with a high degree of acceptance and consideration. Generally we don't have a problem dealing with feelings of unease especially when we know clearly that they are merely temporary. The fact that many smokers don't avoid flights or long work meetings where they cannot smoke proves this. A problem can only arise if we interpret the situation we are in wrongly and narrowing our field of vision.

When looking at things from a broader perspective we understand that all in all the reality of such physical feelings is limited only to people who smoke, or people like us who are on the borderline that precedes the transition to being smokefree. Non-smokers never experience such feelings of unease since their bodies are completely free of nicotine.

From this it is clear to us that we can be in one of two possible situations; either to be smokers and continue to have such feelings all our lives, or to accept with understanding and a certain degree of tranquility the fact that we still have the remnants of symptoms and that they stem from the fact that we were addicted to smoking until recently. The second possibility signals the end of our period of smoking so that the interpretation of every such feeling is that this is a good sign of our approaching freedom.

Set off on the way with the excitement of learning something new just like a child who is learning to ride a bike for the first time. But beyond that, look ahead to a few weeks from now; every day is another step forward toward a 'Safe Harbor' and away from addiction and being chained. What we experience during this short trip is part of the process and meanwhile life in any case goes on as usual. We are, at the end of the day, returning our lives to their natural and right course, and we do this while having fun, in motion, and maintaining our balance.

CHAPTER 5

Actually Stopping to Smoke

You are now at long last equipped with everything you need to embark on a new course. When we reach this stage in our 'Smokefree way' meetings there are some participants who really feel that they have already in practice entered the phase of cessation without noticing it. Others are more stressed and relate to this stage with a somewhat more dramatic approach. One way or another, this is absolutely fine. We have all travelled a long way to reach this state of preparedness – to put the cigarettes behind us and embark confidently on a new way of life.

We have acquired knowledge and a firm awareness that enable us to fully understand where it is that we are heading and how to make the smoothest possible transition to a life of freedom. The way out is, as mentioned, no more than going on the same path but in entirely the opposite direction. You are in a position to make an informed use of the tools you now possess in order to quit, in ways that parallel those that lead us to the addiction in the past.

The actions themselves are entirely in reverse and stem from a diametrically opposite point of reference – becoming smokefree on the basis of a clear understanding of the process and an awareness of what is occurring, instead of being led into an addiction at a time when we lacked understanding and were entirely ignorant of what was happening to us.

The clear expression of the concept of addiction is tangible to us as we feel the urge day after day, hour after hour, to have one cigarette after another. Every cigarette maintains the continuity of this urge. It is a vicious cycle that can be described by a metaphor from the field of cybernetics as generating constant feedback so that one action serves as the cause of the next, and the second leads to yet another action that follows, and so on. If we don't make a change that will put an end to this cycle then this chain of actions can continue forever.

Even if there are those among you who haven't yet entirely noticed it, you should note that in the course of the reading and observation by each and every one of you, the smokescreen that hides the addiction's mechanism has been lifted and your perception of the place that cigarettes occupy in your lives has changed. This state has a significant influence that greatly weakens the mental force nourishing the urge to smoke. Now what is left for us to do is to part from the nicotine itself which constitutes the physical basis driving the urge, and embark on the course that will lead us to being smokefree forever.

BREAKING THE CHAIN

Do you remember your very first cigarette? It is reasonable to assume that you don't. We tend to remember the first few cigarettes rather than a specific one. There is an even more basic question – whether the first cigarettes were the first we ever smoked, or whether they were, in fact, those we smoked when we had at long last learned to inhale all the way into the lungs?

One way or another, the first cigarette we smoked was no big deal for us. I haven't yet come across a smoker able to say that he looked at the first cigarette seriously, stared at it while smoking it, and said to himself: 'Wow, this is the first cigarette in my life. After this one there will be years of smoking, day after day, hour after hour. Today I am taking a big step and abandoning the life I have known till now. I am starting a new chapter in my life – my smoking career.'

We have already said that when we began to smoke we lacked an awareness of what we were embarking on. Had we been able to foresee where these first cigarettes would lead us, the chances that we would have continued to smoke them are very slight.

I have also not come across any smoker who has said that while he was smoking the first cigarettes in his life he said the following to himself: 'I am now smoking my first cigarette. After that I will no longer be a non-smoker. This means that from now on I will no longer be able to be free of nicotine. It is so final. It's a bit stressful isn't it?'

No novice smoker says these things to himself, because no beginner believes that he will ever reach such a state when he has no control over the consumption of cigarettes and will be pushed by an internal need to continue to smoke one cigarette after another.

It has to also be taken into account that a novice smoker is usually a young person who has not ever before experienced addiction. He has no practical concept of what addiction really is and therefore also lacks any alarm sensors that will be triggered and give the appropriate warning. There is no inner voice that wakes up and says 'it seems to you that you are smoking and taking on an image of an independent adult, but you should know that you are going to be a very non-independent customer of the cigarette companies for many years to come.'

Despite the unbelievable ease with which smoking begins, for some reason when you get to the stage of cessation there are smokers who have fears about the transition to a new state and the fact that its implication is that we will never smoke again. There is here some kind of paradox; on the one hand our objective is precisely that – to be free of smoking and smokefree forever – while on the other hand there is a fear of the very fact that stopping to smoke is such a final step.

It is first of all important to understand that the addiction to smoking makes us dependent over a period of years. This weakens us and creates an illusion that the addiction is strong and that we are feeble. The truth is that the reality is exactly the opposite, and that therefore these thoughts will simply fade the moment you embark on a new course and see how simple it is to achieve. Secondly, the fear of something that is very absolute and final stems from the fact that we are breaking the smoking chain all at once. This is an utter change and deters some of you a bit from getting used to the idea.

The step of actually quitting smoking cannot be and doesn't need to be a gradual process. The transition to being smokefree through the multiplication and repetition of our daily tasks without smoking, is in itself a gradual process spanning a few weeks. It is put into practice from the point at which we no longer consume nicotine in any way whatsoever and discontinue all smoking actions. From here on, the process of change begins and the new reality is reinforced progressively and quickly whilst we experience living our daily lives as free people.

Our physical and mental systems cannot absorb this sort of change without there being a complete disconnect from nicotine and from our previous life patterns. This is because we have make room for our bodies to function in an optimal way and to introduce new behavioral patterns in our daily lives.

In fact, the totality of the transition to a new state is an excellent thing and allows us to enjoy the process right from the start. We return control over our lives to our own hands from the very first minute, and lead the process from a position of our own strength and initiative and not out of weakness and fear.

What is said here applies also to the use of substitutes or other aids. Our body needs to be cleansed of nicotine and other poisons and our thinking patterns need to be substantially altered. Attempts to clutch at other means that allegedly ease the cessation of smoking leads to exactly the opposite result.

Such ways reflect an excessive exaggeration of the importance of the addiction, while on the other hand they diminish our self-esteem and our ability to handle quitting. For years we have been prevented from standing up to our addiction and looking it straight in the eye precisely because of such an approach.

What we really need now is to experience the feelings and realize that nothing happens to us as a result of quitting. This is an enormous opportunity for us to reach a point within only two or three days when getting through the day without cigarettes proves to be a pleasant experience. Why should we want to minimize, or in some way lessen this achievement? All these available aids are intended in the first place for those whose quitting does not stem from a clear inner motive or for someone who wrongly attributes such importance to cigarettes that a substitute for them simply has to be found. A smokefree lifestyle is, as its name suggests – free – and real freedom is what we want to achieve. We have no interest in replacing one misconceived behavioral and conceptual frame of reference with another mistaken framework.

I know for a fact that there are also some who read these lines and think to themselves 'what's all this about fear? I'm already waiting for the signal to get going. After the process we've been through while reading this book, who can possibly even imagine longing for a cigarette ever again?'

Well this is indeed so, but as I have pointed out there are differences between people and there are also those who have an excellent understanding of the issues, and yet the strong dependency on cigarettes they developed simply spoofs them. Have no doubt, the fear is only virtual. You will see that as the days and weeks pass, you will be elated by the fact that you are actually 'doing it.' What will preoccupy you is the achievement of being free.

In any case, since such fears are part of the side effects of the addiction, to relieve these concerns completely, I usually give an additional response on this aspect to those who are quitting. I ask, 'what actually worries you at this stage, some vague thought about the more distant future?' If so, then OK, let's decide that for the next two or three months we set free from smoking entirely. Three months is not so final is it? It's really quite a short period. Let's give ourselves the possibility of being really free of smoking and then, when we are not chained to any urge, we'll look at our situation again. I promise you all that there will still be shops and convenience stores selling cigarettes around you. There will be nothing to prevent you from starting to smoke again if that is what you want.

But at least you will have the option to make a real decision as to whether or not you want to start to smoke again. Actually this will be the first time in your lives that you will be really able to decide to become smokers if that is what you want. At least this could be a decision made from a position of awareness and choice, something that you were denied in the past because you became addicted smokers even though it was not your intention.

Your aim is to be free of smoking. This is an experience that is worth having and in your current situation it is also simple and very easy to achieve. After you are completely free of smoking you will have a real choice as to whether it is good and right for you to remain in this state or change it.

If only you had been given this option some years ago. You already know very well deep inside, even before setting off on the way, what is going to happen. You know quite well that when you are really freed of smoking you will have no doubt about which course in life is more appropriate for you. Moreover, already today, before you have actually got there, your desired destination is clear to you, otherwise you wouldn't be reading a book about quitting.

Perhaps you noticed that the way I formulated it was to say that you would always be able to decide whether to start smoking again, and didn't say that you might return to smoking. The reason for that is that when we are free of smoking and two or three months go by, during which we live our daily lives regularly totally without cigarettes and feel great with it, we already fully comply with the term 'smokefree' by definition. That's it, we are out of it. Our smoking cessation has succeeded, we are now non-smokers and we have completely eliminated the need to smoke. Therefore there is no reason on earth why we should want to start a new period of addiction and enslavement.

THE LAST CIGARETTE

When to have the last cigarette? My advice is not to make a big deal over the last cigarette. The truth is that you already smoked what was supposed to be your last cigarette long ago. Don't attribute undue weight to the last cigarette and don't turn the cessation of smoking into a big drama. Though the huge importance of the change you are making and the blessings it brings cannot be exaggerated, the fact is that your life will nonetheless continue as normal and you are merely getting rid of the poison, cleaning out the system, and returning life to its natural and correct course.

When we were young and started to smoke we might have gotten away with it and it could have been said about us: 'OK, like other experiments during adolescence this is also an experiment at creating an image or sending a message to those around you. If, like the other things you are trying out, this too will be over say, within three months, let it be, it's not that terrible.'

But because we all continued to smoke after the three months and became fully fledged smokers, the so called *last* cigarette was actually smoked by us already then. Since then, and to this very day, all the cigarettes we have smoked are in overdraft. We have been in overdraft for years and the debt – which is the addiction itself – has simply continued to swell.

There has to be a cigarette that ends our smoking career just as there was a cigarette that started it. This is only a technical issue and it doesn't matter whether you have it now while you are still reading these lines, or whether you have in fact yourselves decided that the previous cigarette you smoked, no matter when, was actually your last. And perhaps some of you prefer to smoke one or two more in order to arrange your thoughts, steady yourselves, and feel ready and prepared to set off.

Either way is OK, but the main thing is to do it as soon as possible. You have now read it all, internalized it, everything is fresh, and there is motivation and great energies in the air. It is very important that you take advantage of this. The biggest mistake you could make would be to drag out the time for too long, because you could find yourselves turning it into a drama and be caught by the self-deception of just waiting more and more.

Stopping to smoke in practice is only the beginning, no more than that. All the learning and exploring thus far, and all the experiences of being smokefree in the coming days and weeks, are the main thing. Don't wait, just as you didn't delay setting off for the meeting at the Lotto office to pick up a fat check for your winning ticket. Freedom is priceless, and there is no reason why we should go on funding the manufacturers of dry tobacco who rejoice in our misery.

MY OWN CESSATION

My own act of cessation took place late one evening while I was in the office where I was working on an upper floor of a high rise city building. I was alone that evening until late and was reading some material I had assembled about smoking. I had already acquired all the information I needed and was ready to set off on the way to stop smoking.

After I had finished reading I said to myself 'congratulations Tamir, the time has come to end the smoking period in your life.' I took a deep breath and opened my pack of cigarettes to smoke the last one in my life. To my great surprise the pack was empty. I could have given up and stopped smoking right there and then or, alternatively, arranged to get another cigarette which would have required me to leave the office, take one of the elevators going down to the lobby of the building, and buy a pack from the cigarette machine.

I had no preference for a particular option because it was clear to me that the big thing happening here was that my smoking career was ending now, and that this was perhaps one of the most important decisions that I had made in the past few years. It didn't occur to me then that one day I would be involved in a smoking cessation program and certainly not that I would write a book about this. What preoccupied me at that time was the anticipation of changing course and of continuing to be determined and committed to quitting. Exactly like you, I believed that I would succeed and that I was on the right track, but saw in this a serious step that must not be underestimated. It's not every day that we stop smoking, you know.

I however, chose the second option, and went all the way down to the lobby and back to the office to smoke that poor cigarette. I assume I did this because, as you all know, it's always frustrating to open a pack and discover it is empty, even if this is supposed to be your last cigarette ever.

I lit the cigarette and smoked it half way down. I was all alone, taking a good look at the cigarette, the burning paper, the smoke, the yellowing stub, and it all seemed to me so pointless. Years of unawareness and of indulging in the self-deception that this disgusting thing somehow gave me something are now coming to an end. 'It turns out that over the years I have been there with you and for you', I found myself thinking about the cigarettes, even though during that whole time I thought it was the other way around. I am embarking on a new course now and I have no intention of looking back.

What I found odd at that time was that the taste of the cigarette was different and really unpleasant. Strange as it may seem, I hear the same thing fairly often from participants in the program who return from the break having smoked the last cigarette in the lives. It's really very peculiar because the cigarette is, after all, the same cigarette, and all that has changed is our perception.

Given the fact that this doesn't happen to everyone I was inclined to think at the beginning that it only seemed that way to some of us. But when I realized that this phenomenon happens to many participants, I began to reckon that something possibly happens to us at the moment at which we decide to end the smoking chapter in our lives. Suddenly, it is as if there has been some kind of switch in our brains making us aware of things that we hadn't noticed till now.

The cigarette does, indeed, remain the same, and its taste was and remains awful, but at the moment at which we decide to set free it is as if the brain ceases to activate a certain repression mechanism and enables us to taste and smell the cigarette as it really is. It doesn't happen to everyone at the same point in time but it certainly happens to everyone at some time or other.

The main instruction we give participants in our meetings as they go out for their last cigarette is to make sure to find a spot where they can be alone with their own thoughts while they smoke this cigarette. There's no point in making a big fuss about this event, it's just an ending of the chain, but it is preferable that we smoke it when alone, from a position of awareness, and having made a firm decision to use it in order to terminate the period of our lives as smokers.

Back to my own cessation; I stubbed out the half cigarette I was holding, left the office, and on the way home threw the pack with nineteen cigarettes still in it into the trash bin. I was happy that the money I paid for the last pack was for cigarettes that were thrown away rather into my throat and lungs. Since then I haven't smoked a single cigarette and as the days, weeks, and months passed, I noticed that I more and more enjoy being a non-smoker. A heavy non-smoker, remember?

This is how you too are going to feel, like thousands of others who have become smokefree, and there is no greater gift that you can give yourselves. Take a few minutes if you need to. Sit by yourselves and arrange your thoughts. This is the time to take a big step in your lives that will lead you to a freedom and an independence that you haven't experienced for years. Do it. Do it now.

CHAPTER 6

Terminology

It is now very important to pay special attention to the way in which we speak of our setting free from smoking, both with those around us and in particular with ourselves. We are now in a process of change and a correct definition of concepts will help us to be confident and clear about our state.

Try not to refer to it as 'a break from smoking', but rather to think of it in terms of 'I am turning into a non-smoker' or becoming 'smokefree.' A break is inherently temporary, whereas the change we are making is fundamental and permanent. It is essential that we use the right words to describe things because what we say to ourselves also becomes entrenched as a message in our subconscious, and it is precisely there that we will be directing our acts and deeds in the coming period.

If someone asks you 'are you on a break from smoking now?' I wouldn't expect you to correct him by pointing out his mistaken definition. There are common conversational phrases that people regularly use and it's not our intention right now to change those practices. I too, both in speech and in writing, occasionally use the accepted and common terminology. It is certainly possible to respond to the question in the affirmative, but the important thing is for us to immediately remind ourselves that 'I'm not on a break from smoking, I'm becoming a non-smoker.' These words will echo in your heads and will make an impression.

In case you hear a smoker saying 'Yes, this is a really bad habit', remind yourselves that this is not a habit but an addiction. To change habits there is no need for advanced preparation and there is no need to deal with physical senses and misconceptions. In contrast, setting free from an addiction requires thorough preparation as well as consistent and informed progress toward our objective.

It is important that we be alert to the self-deception employed by our smoking friends, as they attempt to paint a picture for themselves of a softer reality in order to avoid confronting the situation as it really is. No one gets stuck with habits that they cannot change, but people do get stuck with addiction.

The same goes for the declaration 'it's all in your head' which smokers warmly embrace in order to sum everything up with a simple explanation. It's a kind of magical declaration that smokers say to themselves and which means something like 'when I decide that I want to stop, I will simply stop without a problem.' Meaning that there is no need for guidance, no need for internal scrutiny, nor is there a need to examine the addiction's mechanism. Why should there be? It is, after all, 'all in the head'. All you have to do is simply decide, just like that, and that's it, you stop smoking. Yeah, right.

Ask a smoker who says such a thing whether he knows someone who stopped in this way. If it's really so simple is it logical that millions of people all over the world feel that they are stuck with cigarettes and can't set free from them?

Smokers tell themselves this story in order to leave some kind of an open door of hope that one day they will be able, just like that, to stop smoking. Since today for them it is not so, they try to create an excuse as to why. The logical explanation that comes to their minds is that they have simply not reached that stage of readiness at which it is time to stop. That's all there is to it. According to this perspective when the day finally comes and they feel that it is time to stop, they will simply do so without it being a problem. Unfortunately such a day never dawns.

Though it is true that the mental part in the process is of great importance, yet our ability to reach the right realizations, gain an understanding of the addiction, and actually setting free, never come 'just like that'. Only someone who doesn't understand the addiction to smoking remains unaware of the fact that every smoking day reinforces the addiction rather than weakening it. The fact that someone reaches the stage when he's fed up with being a smoker doesn't in the slightest affect his embedded need to continue smoking.

If somebody nonetheless tries to dupe you by saying that he knows someone who succeeded in setting free of smoking 'just like that', start to ask a few questions about the background of this 'someone'. It is reasonable to assume that you will quickly discover that there was a critical reason, some sort of major influence that has affected this person and which led him to make the change. Don't be caught up in the illusions of other smokers. No one ever gets up one morning and for no particular reason and without preparation decides that he's ending his smoking career simply because that's what he feels like doing.

In no way is it our purpose to confront smokers. In fact, my advice is to talk as little as possible about your smoking cessation. Smokers are unable to understand, and you will certainly not be able in a brief and general conversation to pass on to them what you have learned in a cessation program or in a whole book.

It's best to be modest about it and notice how your smoking friends hurry to suppress the fact that you have set yourselves free. It's not so simple for them to accept the reality that you are all sitting together as usual but for some reason already once, twice, or more, you are not smoking together with them. And yet you are still able to have a mutually pleasant evening or a meal, without you're not smoking being a problem for you.

For smokers it is hard to come to terms with this fact because, happy though they may be for you, so far as they themselves are concerned, you're stopping to smoke creates a problem for them. It is a reminder of their condition and is interpreted as a message signaling their inferiority in relation to non-smokers. Every smoker that leaves the 'group' and switches sides, reinforces this message.

We mustn't forget that we are no better than them and that we have no reason to patronize anyone. That is how it also was with us when others around stopped smoking; we didn't really notice it because what smokers generally do in this situation is to try repress and ignore it.

During the first days after I had stopped smoking I spent an evening with two of my best friends. They, of course, smoked and were surprised that I was no longer smoking. Because I was a bit discreet about it and presented it as something that wasn't particularly preoccupying me, they avoided interrogating me and harassing me with annoying questions, and the evening proceeded as usual.

Only a few months later, when one of the two friends came to consult me about the possibility of him stopping to smoke, did he tell me that after I left for home following that meeting, they talked about my not having smoked while the three of us were together. Their response was to make a bet of honor. One of them bet that I would return to being a smoker within a week, while the other was a little bit more generous and bet that I would go back to smoking within two weeks to a month.

That is how the suppression mechanism works among smokers. From their point of view the possibility that I may never go back to smoking was likely to be a reminder in some way of their vulnerability in relation to the addiction to smoking. Therefore, the natural tendency is to ignore such a possibility. Had either one of them raised the issue again since the bet? Not at all. The weeks and months that passed proved that neither had been right in his estimation and it was much more comfortable for both of them to ignore the issue than to relate to it.

Don't 'try' and stop. When you say to your friends or to yourselves 'I'm trying to stop smoking', you are making it needlessly hard for yourself. First of all we have already said that we are becoming smokefree and not merely stopping to smoke without changing our perception. But beyond this, relating to the change as 'an attempt' puts us in a position of inferiority right from the start.

Almost every action of ours in life is an attempt, but we don't define things that way in most cases. We try to get to work every morning; we try to get out to do the shopping; we try to cook dinner and we try to meet up with our friends. Generally we also succeed in achieving these tasks but we don't define every situation as an attempt.

When arranging to meet a friend in a coffee shop we don't usually say to him 'I will try to get there' but rather we say 'I'll get to the coffee shop at six.' It's obvious that we are only going to try and get there; we'll try and leave work on time; try and avoid being caught up in an accident on the way; try and avoid traffic jams and parking problems. All these are attempts. But in the way we talk there is generally a distinction between things that seem to us to be more certain to happen – that in daily speech we will express with full confidence – and those things about which we really have a greater degree of uncertainty – which we will define as attempts. Though we don't pay attention to this we in fact are talking about differences that mainly stem from our subjective feeling towards a given situation.

Trying or trials, in the professional sense, relates to experiments generally associated with the lab and research. When we carry out an experiment it confirms the fact that there is no clear certainty as to the outcome. Similarly, in daily language, when we for example say that we are trying a new recipe it suggests that there is no certainty as to whether or not the dish will be tasty. When we take on a new team member at work we usually refer to his period of integration as a trial. We are uncertain whether he will succeed in the job or not.

Since it is up to us to define how to relate to the situations we're in and to our actions, we have to realize that defining ourselves as smokefree and deciding with a high degree of certainty that this is so, will also entrench this reality in the right place in our subconscious. What's more, the degree of certainty is really high. Not only that, it is actually more certain than almost any other thing that we do or set out to do.

The reason for this is that this change in our life's course is not dependent on almost any external factors, as opposed to the meeting with a friend at a coffee shop which is dependent on our getting to the place, on it not raining or snowing which could prevent us from getting there, on our car not getting stuck on the way, on the coffee shop not being closed for some temporary reason, and on a number of additional things that could happen.

In contrast to this, becoming smokefree is dependent exclusively on us and the extent of our determination to achieve it. There are absolutely no external factors forcing us to smoke. In fact, when we correctly understand the relevant matters, we become aware that in all circumstances the advantage is always in experiencing reality as free people. Our determination and our aspiration to achieve the lifestyle we have decided to attain will definitely get us there – no question about it. There is no reason why we shouldn't stand tall and reinforce our decision.

There is an essential rule that you should remember – the extent of our determination and confidence has a direct influence on the speed and ease with which we complete the desired change.

A BRIEF SUMMARY OF THE MAIN GUIDELINES TO CESSATION

- Setting free is an outcome and a direct continuation of the process of examination and review. Smoking is a phenomenon that is external to us and has gained control over our lives over time, too much time. The realization that this whole addiction is external is marvelous and possesses huge power to guide us in setting free.

- The physical feelings, if there are such, are a very temporary experience during the first two or three days – these are the days when we cross the border on the way to a 'Safe Harbor'.

- Since the dependence on cigarettes is a cycle that we are responsible for having unintentionally created, once we have removed it from our lives it will soon seem to us as if that dependency had never existed.

- This is an opportunity to see life and experience it without smoking, in the knowledge that all the feelings of the first few days are also a onetime experience. In a short time we will already not feel anything special.

- Our self-definition is not only dependent on what we consciously say to ourselves. The more we do something and repeat the action, the more that action passes from the conscious into the subconscious. When we carry out exactly the same actions without smoking we are sending a message to the

226

subconscious – this is our new lifestyle. With every such action we reinforce our reality as free people.

- Our brain is designed to absorb this repetition of actions without a cigarette in exactly the same way as it absorbed the multiplication and repetition of our smoking in the process of addiction. Thus, in setting free from smoking, it turns out that we use the very same technique that in the past led us to becoming smokers.

- To stop smoking completely is a process no more difficult than to start smoking. For most people who do it correctly the process is, in fact, easier. Every feeling can be accepted by us as a sort of experience we have to go through, and accordingly it is possible for us to absorb it with a high degree of acceptance and consideration.

- Actual cessation of smoking cannot be and does not have to be gradual. In addition, the use of substitutes or other aids is totally wrong.

- Don't make a big deal out of the last cigarette, it is just a technical matter and all it does is to end the chain. Make sure you smoke this cigarette when you are alone.

- Start thinking in terms of 'I am becoming a non-smoker' or 'smokefree'. What we say to ourselves also becomes entrenched in our subconscious, and it is exactly where we will be directing our actions and deeds in the period just ahead.

- It is preferable that you be modest and talk as little as possible about your smoking cessation both with smokers as well as with non-smokers.

- Don't relate to the change as if you are 'trying'. Attaching a high degree of certainty to our self-definition as smokefree will also entrench this reality in the right place in our subconscious. The transition to being smokefree is dependent only on us and our determination.

Part Four:

A New and Great State

CHAPTER 1

A Tangible improvement in the Quality of Life

This short section which ends the book is intended to help you maintain your astonishing achievement. Up till now what we have mainly dealt with are the issues revolving around the addiction and the process of setting free from it. Now we have the opportunity of spelling out how amazing your setting free from smoking really is. It will be no exaggeration to say that you are actually regaining your life.

As smokers we tend to play down the many implications that smoking has for our lives and the price that this reality might exact from us. Accordingly, it wasn't right to reflect in a profound way on this aspect in the course of reading the book. It wouldn't have helped us to quit and it would have diverted the discussion to the external reasons for quitting, while the right starting point for setting free is, in fact, the rejection of the addiction itself rather than a fear of what its expected outcome may be.

But now that we are in the process of returning to the natural and correct course in life, we will be able to see the benefits we are gaining which will improve the quality of our lives, both immediately and in the longer term, wherever we look. From the physical aspect the change will be sensed from head to toe, in every organ. There isn't one that will not benefit.

Our skin will regain its vitality, all sorts of different spots will disappear and the accelerated aging of the skin will be halted. Our teeth will once again be whiter and cleaner. Moreover, the prevention of various oral health problems will save us a lot of trouble. Research carried out in this field has shown that the combination of smoke and saliva in the mouth seriously damages the saliva's efficacy in protecting the oral cavity. Our lungs cleanse themselves quickly and the transference of oxygen will demand less of an effort from them and the heart – our life pump.

The throat and vocal chords also get cleansed. I once talked on the phone to a woman who had quit after decades of smoking. When she smoked her voice had been coarse and abrasive. When I spoke to her again after she quit I couldn't at first recognize her voice which had returned to being youthful and feminine in a way I hadn't known it to be in the past.

The narrowing of arteries and capillaries stops, the blood's texture becomes smoother, and problems such as various aches and pains in our hands and legs, chronic fatigue, a constant cough, all disappear from our lives.

No matter to what extent we may have gone to avoid relating to the price we pay in terms of our health by smoking, this reality is inevitable. It cannot be that poisoning and constant chocking won't adversely influence our body systems. Fortunately, for most of us this is a slow and gradual process so that serious harm may only occur after a very prolonged period. In contrast, the cleansing process and the return of the systems to optimal functioning are fast and efficient.

This is not the time or place to explain the health implications of smoking. The aim here is actually to spur you to relate to the abundance of vitality, healthy and energizing experiences you are about to have in the period ahead. In the coming months you are going to enjoy many gifts of life that have been withheld from you till now, and there is no reason for spoiling the happiness by revealing information that for you as non-smokers is no longer relevant.

But when you get used to the new state so that a life of being smokefree becomes the established rule for you, and when you feel sufficiently confident and comfortable, do yourselves a big favor. Get on to the internet or some other source of information and read a bit about the link between smoking and health.

Don't say to yourselves 'well… that's obvious and there's no point in wasting time on it.' This is being said by the same inner voice in your heads that used to stand on guard over the years to prevent you from being exposed to this information. Once you are completely set free you will no longer need this suppression mechanism because you will no longer be concerned about being exposed to such material.

It is vital that this suppression mechanism be exiled, and that you open yourselves up to this information which you learned to ignore in such a dedicated way as if you had developed a unique skill for it. You should do this to reinforce your acknowledgment and grasp of your new lives. This is also important to help you completely understand what it is that the cigarette manufacturers got you into so that they could get rich on the back of your suffering.

A physical improvement and better health are only a beginning. You're about to gain an hour and a half a day of extra time. Do you realize what an extra one and a half hours of free time means? It's not only that a significant number of you are actually going to live much longer, but the prolongation of our lives becomes expressed by making the most of every single day.

Though smoking deprives the average smoker of between one and a half and two hours a day, it could be argued that we nevertheless don't stop everything we do every time we have a cigarette. There are those who can work while smoking, surf the web, watch a serial or a movie, smoke during a meeting for coffee, and so on. This is true, but there is nonetheless a great deal of time wasting linked to the cigarettes that isn't taken into account. Buying the cigarettes and making sure that there is always change for the next pack; always ensuring that you have a lighter; cleaning ashtrays; searching for smoking areas when you get to some event; and when you go out for smoking breaks from places where smoking is forbidden – such as workplaces or shopping malls for example – you sometimes have to go a pretty long way to reach an open area, and so on.

An hour and a half may not be a tight estimate but there is no doubt that a great deal of extra time is freed up. It has to be understood that time means more than time taken up in actions, but also of time taken up in thought. Thoughts such as 'how many have I smoked today?' 'Perhaps I've already smoked too much?' 'How many cigarettes do I have left?' 'Perhaps I should get another pack?' 'Perhaps I'll get it later'? All these will belong to the past. We no longer have to preoccupy ourselves with these "fateful" questions.

More energy and more self-confidence. When the body functions much better and the mind is free of useless questions, there is a greater degree of alertness and motivation to do things, to initiate, to be more active. This is added to the enormous feeling of achievement that we have succeeded in ridding ourselves of the addiction that for years was the source of intimidation and paralyzed us. We are beginning to look at life differently. If we have reached the point when we can stand up to our addiction to smoking and neutralize it, this provides us with an opening to shape our lifestyles in a range of other areas which we want to improve.

Though the 'Smokefree way' program is a format for overcoming our problem with smoking, its foundations can certainly be applied to other changes we want to bring about in our lives. After setting free of smoking, changing other elements in our lives seems like a much easier task.

We can now allow ourselves to be who we are and as we are. For years, in a range of situations, we deprived ourselves of the right to feel comfortable being simply as we really are; without any pretenses; without being influenced by the pressure to smoke wherever we happen to be; without having to create and nurture superficial arguments to justify for a pattern of behavior which is entirely based on addiction.

Experiencing real freedom is something that we have been denied for years. Within a few days you will begin to understand this. You will go through entire days without the feelings and the urges to go out for a cigarette break. You will sit with friends or participate at events and you will see that to be smokefree and to not need to go out for a smoking break allows you to enjoy a whole event without interruptions. For entire days you will be able to work without wandering off for cigarette breaks all the time, without the incessant thoughts of whether to go out for a cigarette break now or delay it a bit longer. Suddenly you will see that everything seems to be just right. You will have the real freedom to do whatever you want to do and whenever you want to do it. No longer subjected to the authority of the 'lord of smoke.'

When you go out of a hall or restaurant to accompany your smoking friends you will feel the enormous difference between you and them. When they ask you to accompany them for a cigarette break, you will be going by choice and at ease while they will be going because of a compulsion and a constraint. They will chat to you as usual and not pay any attention to the cigarette they are smoking, for the simple reason that they are not really going out for a cigarette break but rather are being *taken* out for a break in order to supply the body with another dose of nicotine.

Metaphorically it could be said they are not smoking the cigarette, but that rather it is the cigarette that is smoking them. Meaning that they are pawns in the hands of the addiction, they are not in control of the situation nor are they acting out of free choice.

When they finish the cigarette and you ask them if everything is OK and whether they are content, they will answer 'you bet... I simply had to have that cigarette.' You will be able to see how both in thought and speech they confirm their action. At this point in time don't say anything to them. You should not try to prove them wrong because they are not in a position to accept the information. When a smoker needs to calm the tension, his thinking is short term – to resolve the problem. Any general comment about the phenomenon might only serve to put them under even more pressure. If you feel an obligation to say something, speak only about yourselves and pass on a message about how great it is to be outside the smoking cycle. Let them come to you to get advice about a solution to their problem.

CHAPTER 2

Being Prepared For Flashbacks

Beyond the acquisition of knowledge about the addiction and the change of perception, the process of setting free from smoking in practice is mainly based on multiplication and repetition of actions and situations. This enables our subconscious to absorb the new reality and turn it into an integral part of our lives.

In everything concerned with our daily lives things happen fairly rapidly since our routine life is, for the most part, somewhat monotonous and allows us on a daily basis to return and reinforce the exact same situations; finishing meals, drinking coffee or tea, telephone conversations, breaks, and a whole range of different activities. All of these amount to the critical mass of our lifestyle, and as a result of repeatedly engaging in them the assimilation of our reality as non-smokers is reinforced from day to day.

Thus within a few weeks we reach a quantitative and continuous mass of situations without smoking and the disengagement from the old lifestyle becomes completely validated and stable. In the time that passes we get used to the freedom and our self-definition as smokefree becomes something regular and obvious.

We have to take into account that the changes in our lifestyle and in the patterns of the subconscious, are put into practice in all the places and situations we find ourselves in. If a situation that was connected to the addiction in the past doesn't arise, we cannot affect the change.

This, as we have shown, is because we need an actual occasion to occur in order for us to apply to it a new behavioral pattern to replace an old pattern. It is the only way that enables us to remove the mental conditioning that was previously connected to a certain situation.

The implication is that in relation to particular cases that are infrequent and are not part of our routine, there is a possibility that they will not arise in the near future. As a result, dormant thinking patterns and conditionings which we have not yet had a chance to alter may remain with us, for the simple reason that we haven't come across the situations to which they are connected.

This could happen during unusually stressful situations such as examinations, or dismissal from work, or an unforeseen economic crisis. Sometimes it can be connected to worries about your health or the health of a close relative. The common denominator is that we are talking about situations that are unforeseeable and which have a powerful emotional impact on us. Sometimes the context can be a positive one rather than a situation of distress; a surprise party or the winning of a prize or the bestowal of a special honor. In any event, as said, these are situations in which we find ourselves not so well prepared.

In all these cases an old and dormant thinking pattern can suddenly be awakened that will link the situation you are in to the smoking of a cigarette – a kind of rapidly flashing thought and perhaps also an odd sensation that you may experience for a few seconds. We refer to these situations as 'flashbacks'.

It happens every now and again to almost everyone and can be a bit stressful since sometimes a significant period of time can elapse before a flashback appears. This can occur at a point in time when we already identify ourselves as completely smokefree. In such a case the flashback can come as a surprise to us since we don't experience any need, and it doesn't cross our minds that we might get a reminder of the old lifestyle.

These are the last remnants of the addiction that have still not been erased from our consciousness because those particular situations that are relatively rare have not crossed our path so far. This is an excellent opportunity for us to get rid of these last patterns, but we must recognize the possibility of such an occurrence and be prepared for it. We cannot artificially initiate situations in which a flashback appears.

If we are prepared for it, then the flashback cannot unbalance us and we can relate to it in exactly the same way as we have related to all the other life situations – as an opportunity to go through an experience that aligns itself with our reality of being free people.

Flashbacks pose no danger and they pass very quickly so long as they are understood by us and we are prepared for them. The only preparation we should make is taking place right now with the reading of this text. We are acknowledging that such a phenomenon may occur, and that's it. Beyond that there is no need for us to preoccupy ourselves with this.

However, someone who is unaware that he may be confronted by a flashback is liable to misunderstand the reality and sometimes this could even endanger the great achievement of freedom.

To illustrate this at our meetings I generally tell the story of what happened to a close friend of mine. My friend is a successful lawyer whose main work is in real estate transactions. Accordingly, he holds significant sums of money in a trust account at the bank belonging to clients who are buying properties. His line of business also involves having working relations with various building contractors. My friend is an ex-smoker and at the time of this incident I am referring to, he had been on a break from smoking for about three years.

As fate would have it, one of the contractors in touch with my lawyer friend was caught up in financial difficulties and debts. In desperation the contractor decided to issue a forged letter in the name of the lawyer, instructing the bank to transfer to the contractor the sum of half a million dollars from the trust account held by the lawyer. The contractor went to the bank's local branch and presented the letter. The bank clerks who knew both the contractor and the lawyer very well failed in their duty and offhandedly transferred the funds to the contractor. This was despite the fact that according to the rules they were obliged to first of all verify by phone, as well as by other means, that there was authorization to pay the sum and that the letter was genuine.

Not much time passed before the missing sum prevented the execution of other transactions on the account, and the bank's account manager got in touch with the lawyer to be updated as to when the missing sum would be credited to the account. The lawyer, who had no idea that monies had been fraudulently removed from the account, was greatly alarmed and rushed to the bank to find out what had happened.

When the documents were shown to him he was utterly shocked – he, after all, hadn't ever signed such documents and there was no basis for the funds being transferred to the contractor. The lawyer called the contractor for clarification and the contractor in turn admitted to what he had done. He explained that he had fallen on very hard times and asked for forgiveness. He added that the money was no longer in his possession and said that he was aware that he would have to stand trial and bear the consequences.

My lawyer friend knew that the money would be returned to his account by the bank because the clerks at the branch had been negligent, and it was also clear to him that no one could legitimately complain about his own role – he had merely been the victim of a fraudulent act.

When he left the bank, the lawyer was so angry and disappointed that it unbalanced him. Such incidents of forgery and fraud are not something that normative people are used to deal with. As if out of nowhere the pressure and stress he experienced at the time brought up just one thought and one thought only – 'I must have cigarette'. Yes, however unrelated it may seem, the great frustration and the feeling of shock aroused in him an old thought that linked the very intense tension to a cigarette.

Though this is an extreme example it is nonetheless illustrative of a flashback. Even though for a number of years the lawyer hadn't smoked, and even though cigarettes and their taste were already alien to him, the conditioning that was interpreted by him to mean 'have a smoke now' was awakened.

This re-awakening occurred out of a situation which called for an act of spite. The conscious thinking was aware that the cigarette wouldn't help, and was also aware that the taste of the cigarette after such a long time without smoking would be repulsive and suffocating. But the lawyer, who had stopped smoking about three years prior to this incident, did not get proper instruction and didn't have the good fortune of becoming fully free. He more fitted the definition of a 'smoker on a break' than 'ex-smoker' despite the long period he had gone through without smoking.

When the smoking cessation is not based on a clear approach that involves a changed perception, and when it is not clearly understood that cessation is not solely concerned with the external change of refraining from smoking, then even if a significant period of time passes by without smoking, a person can still find himself in an erratic frame of mind and experiencing a craving that seems to arise for no particular reason.

Situations of such intensity are not likely to happen to you because your starting point in your smoking cessation is far more stable, and is the outcome of a fundamental decision as to how you define yourselves.

Since from a chronological aspect we are implementing the cessation of smoking following an examination of the addiction and a recognition of the course of life we wish to follow as smokefree people, we are actually turning the cessation in practice into a process that implements the very reality which we are aiming for.

For us, setting free comes from the confident knowledge that the addiction is not part of our personality but is rather the seizure of control by an alien factor which we have the power to eliminate. In addition to the process of becoming smokefree we become immune to fluctuations of external events and moods. It is clear to us that all of life's events will be managed in the best possible way when our physical and mental systems are cleansed of nicotine and its repercussions.

For this reason the flashbacks that we might have will not be as shaking for us as they would be for 'smokers on a break'. For us, flashbacks can only awaken the last remnants of the old thinking patterns in our subconscious which we have to let go.

You have nothing to fear from the appearance of flashbacks. You need only be aware of the possibility that you will come across them and let them pass you by quickly. The great importance of clarifying this issue is to avoid you being perplexed or stressed if and when you come across an odd feeling – be it even months after you are set free and feel great. In addition, it is also essential that you be aware that such incidents are common and not make the mistake of thinking that this is a phenomenon that is unique to you and that you have in some way not acted correctly.

By the way, as for my friend the lawyer, after a period of two years or so since that unfortunate incident during which he returned to smoking a pack a day, he came to me for a private session. He was of course freed from the oppressive addiction and became smokefree – this time for good.

CHAPTER 3

A New Era

During the reading of this book we have been on a journey which had a number of stages. We started with clarifying the addiction experience – perceived by smokers as a need that has to be fulfilled. We reviewed the influence of nicotine on a person's body systems and the brain. We continued with an examination of the addiction's psychological structure and its influence on our subconscious, and from there we progressed towards actually setting free and our becoming smokefree forever.

At the beginning we had a great fear of dealing with the phenomenon of the addiction altogether. This is one of those unique subjects about which at an early stage many of us have a fear not only of failing but also a fear of succeeding.

As smokers, our enormous dependency on cigarettes creates the initial perception that if we stop smoking we will be deprived of something all the time and that our personality will be diminished in some way. It doesn't at all occur to us that perhaps a life with a permanent feeling of deprivation is the fate only of smokers, and that perhaps setting free of smoking will bring with it the kind of stability and calmness which for years already we have not experienced.

It is amazing to discover just how easy it is to change course and embark on the right path of life if you only acquire the information about, and awareness of, the phenomenon of smoking. So long as we don't acknowledge that our perceptions in relation to smoking are misconceived, it will seem to us that our way in life with a cigarette in hand and a pack in our pocket gives us something. The moment we begin to understand that this way distances us from everything that is right and good for us we start to lose interest in it.

The 'Smokefree way' program presents us with a more natural and more correct way of life. Our acceptance of this great possibility can only come when we have reached a point that enables us to confront and validate our way as smokers on the one hand with our way as smokefree on the other.

It is reasonable to assume that no smoker who understood exactly how the addiction's mechanism works would be willing to come to terms with it. The fact that he was being manipulated by a system of inevitable processes, compelling him to persist with his smoking for the benefit of the major cigarette corporations, would be simply unacceptable. No novice smoker consciously takes on board the fact that he is about to become chained to cigarettes for many years to come.

At some stage in life we simply find ourselves stuck with the cigarettes without an understanding of how this happened to us. You nonetheless chose not to be deterred and to read the book, and discovered that when the picture becomes clearer things are much simpler and easier to implement than we initially thought.

Since mass production of cigarettes began some one hundred and thirty years ago, the smoking phenomenon has grown to quite monstrous proportions. As of today there are more than a billion smokers in the world, which means that within the adult population one in every three or four people smokes, depending on which area of the world you live in.

Statistically, nearly all smokers begin their smoking career before the age of twenty. Every day a new generation of tomorrow's smokers takes its first steps in replacing the previous generation. When these new smokers are in the early stages of addiction they are generally most definitely not open to realizing that they are simply losing their freedom.

Only lately are there indications, the first road signs that something in this tendency is changing. Youngsters, mainly in some parts of the United States, are beginning to reject smoking from a social point of view. They are wiser than the previous generations. With the exposure to endless information via the internet together with governmental investments in advertising and education, a different social approach is beginning to develop which scorns the fictitious image presenting smoking as fun, cool, and trendy.

However, until this trend continues and grows sufficiently to make a real difference to the statistics, people will go on becoming addicted to cigarettes. Meanwhile, an entire industry that is based on manufacturing a sham product that obliges the consumers to go on smoking every day and every hour, will persist in poisoning and polluting our world.

In the meantime, every one of us who liberates himself from the chains of the addiction and embarks on the new course of freedom, passes on the message to the smokers left behind that it is possible and beneficial to quit smoking and that all that it requires is a willingness to see the reality as it really is.

My vision is to spread the method of the 'Smokefree way' program to every place which it is possible to reach in which smokers can be found. I want the book to be accessible to smokers in every place where cigarettes have gained a foothold, a kind of antidote that will be obtainable in convenience stores, in coffee shops and bars, as well as through the internet. To be smokefree is a basic right that we must all take advantage of. We deserve this freedom, and this freedom will prevail.

12737919R00142

Printed in Great Britain
by Amazon.co.uk, Ltd.,
Marston Gate.